This book belongs to:

............Grace................

..Kindergarten.2006.........

Written by Kath Smith
Illustrated by Caroline Jayne Church
Designed by Andrea Newton
Language consultant: Betty Root

This is a Parragon Publishing book
This edition published in 2005

Parragon Publishing
Queen Street House
4 Queen Street
Bath BA1 1HE, UK

Copyright © Parragon 2002
Printed in China

ISBN 1-40546-477-1

The Little Friends
Fairies are Fun

p

Silly Fairy Lily

Lily was a fairy who
Was always lots of fun.
But sometimes Lily's jokes went wrong
And upset everyone.

She wasn't really naughty,
But she didn't take much care.
In her trail, she always left
Disaster everywhere.

She borrowed Heather's magic book,
And let the spells escape.
She stirred her drink with Daisy's wand,
Until it lost its shape.

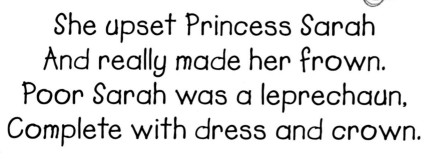

She upset Princess Sarah
And really made her frown.
Poor Sarah was a leprechaun,
Complete with dress and crown.

8

Sir Dave was most annoyed one day.
"She made my best horse shrink!
What a silly girl!" he cried.
"If only she would think!"

One day Fairy Lily met
The nephew of Sir Dave,
And saw the trouble that is caused
By those who misbehave!

He used her wand for fighting,
And spilled her fairy dust.
Then raced around while Lily cried,
"Oh, do please stop! You must!"

As he smashed some glasses
(She heard the awful clink),
Lily yelled in horror,
"If only you would think!"

As soon as she had spoken,
She laughed aloud in glee.
"I've heard those words before,"
She said, "but they were said to me!"

"I guess I should be grateful
To you, you little tyke,
For showing me so clearly
Just what my ways are like."

Now Lily is more careful,
And looks at all the facts.
Before she does a silly thing,
She thinks before she acts!

Clever Fairy Heather

Heather was the smartest
Of the fairies in the land.
So people always came to her—
She loved to lend a hand.

No matter WHAT the problem was,
WHATEVER it involved,
As soon as Heather tackled it,
You knew it would be solved.

"Don't you worry!" she would smile,
As helpful as can be.
"I will find an answer.
Just you wait and see!"

Now Heather had her problems, too,
Which she really longed to share.
But no one took the time to listen—
They did not seem to care.

When Heather tried to tell her friends
About her little troubles,
All they seemed to want to do
Was speak of their own muddles.

Though Heather was a patient girl,
She finally slammed her door,
And shouted in her loudest voice,
"I won't listen anymore!"

The other fairies were amazed.
"Has Heather gone on strike?
It really isn't like her ...
it's just not Heather-like!"

Then Daisy saw just what was wrong,
"Oh, now I understand!
When Heather has a problem,
Who gives a helping hand?"

Lily blushed a shade of pink.
"I really must agree.
Because I don't say thank you
Whenever she helps me."

"It's time that we said thank you
For all her good advice,
And showed her just how much we care
By doing something nice."

So Lily gave her bluebells,
And polished Heather's wings.
While lazy Daisy cleaned her house
And fixed some broken things.

"I might be smart," Heather said,
And hugged them happily.
"But not enough to realize
What friends you are to me!"

Lazy Fairy Daisy

Daisy was a fairy who
Was lazy as can be.
Whenever someone asked for help,
She'd yawn and say, "Why me?"

When other fairies teased her,
And called her lazybones,
She'd mutter, "Words can't hurt me.
They're not like sticks and stones."

Why she was so idle
Was very hard to say.
(The only reason was, I fear,
That she was born that way!)

So while the others rushed around
Preparing for the ball,
Daisy lounged around and yawned,
"What's the matter with you all?"

She watched them cut their costumes out,
Then neatly sew each dress.
But Daisy didn't lend a hand—
She just could not care less!

Even Princess Lucy,
Who liked to dream a lot,
Had made herself a costume,
But Daisy just would not!

The night before the summer ball
Poor Daisy saw her fate.
"I haven't got a costume,
And now it is too late!"

"Don't worry," whispered Lucy,
Who had a bright idea.
"You will have a dress to wear.
Now wipe away that tear"

Soon Daisy's friends were busy.
They stitched throughout the night,
Until they'd made a costume
That fitted her just right.

"Oh, thank you!" exclaimed Daisy,
Smiling now with pleasure.
"Today I've learned a lesson—
And one I'll always treasure!

For when there is a job to do—
Now I understand—
The work is done in half the time,
If we all lend a hand!

I won't be lazy anymore—
Not when there's work to do!
So when this ball is over,
I'll straighten up for you!"

29

Legalizing Drugs

by Meryl Loonin

LUCENT Overview Series

LUCENT BOOKS
An imprint of Thomson Gale, a part of The Thomson Corporation

Woodland High School

THOMSON
★
GALE
™

Detroit • New York • San Francisco • San Diego • New Haven, Conn. • Waterville, Maine • London • Munich

To Neil, Hana, and Jonah

© 2006 Thomson Gale, a part of The Thomson Corporation.

Thomson and Star Logo are trademarks and Gale and Lucent Books are registered trademarks used herein under license.

For more information, contact
Lucent Books
27500 Drake Rd.
Farmington Hills, MI 48331-3535
Or you can visit our Internet site at http://www.gale.com

LIBRARY OF CONGRESS CATALOGING-IN-PUBLICATION DATA

Loonin, Meryl.
  Legalizing drugs / by Meryl Loonin.
    p. cm. — (The overview series)
  Includes bibliographical references and index.
  ISBN 1-56006-357-2 (hard cover : alk. paper)
  1. Drug legalization—United States. 2. Narcotics, Control of—United States. 3. Drug abuse—Government policy—United States. I. Title. II. Series.
  HV5825.L648 2005
  362.29'1561—dc22

                                                                2004030770

Printed in the United States of America

Contents

Introduction

IN JANUARY 2002, the U.S. government launched a new television advertising campaign aimed at stopping young people from taking illegal drugs. The ads premiered during the Super Bowl, one of the most watched TV events of the year. One of the ads featured an image of AK-47 assault weapons, followed by the line, "Where do terrorists get their money? If you buy drugs, some of it might come from you." In another, a group of teens took turns blaming themselves for global terror: "I helped murder families in Colombia"; "I helped a bomber get a fake passport"; "I helped blow up buildings."[1] The message was hard-hitting and clear. People who buy or use illegal drugs such as marijuana or cocaine support terrorism around the world, since, in many countries, terrorist groups raise money for their activities by producing and selling illegal drugs.

In print, on the airwaves, and in Internet chat rooms, people debated the impact of the new ads. Among the many opinions expressed, some people said that attempts by the ads' sponsor, the U.S. government–funded Office of National Drug Control Policy (ONDCP), to link teen drug use to terrorists were so exaggerated that few young people would believe them. Similar scare tactics had been tried before, but had done little to deter teenagers from using drugs. Others argued that the ads were hypocritical, since they played alongside beer commercials that linked alcohol use with beach parties, popular music, and good times. Alcohol is a legal drug, but kills far more Americans, and young people, through drunk driving, reckless behavior, and aggression than any other illegal substance. Some people, who oppose America's current drug policies, attacked the ads as misleading. They said that it is not simply the use or sale of drugs such as marijuana, heroin, or cocaine that funds terrorists around the world, but the reliance on a black market to buy and sell drugs, an illegal market without rules or regulations in which violence and corruption are commonplace. If these drugs were subject to the same kind of rules under which beer or cars are bought and sold, illegal terrorist groups would be forced to rely on other sources of funding.

Government sponsored media and advertising campaigns are often aimed at stopping young people from buying and using illegal drugs.

Drug Prohibition

Yet unlike beer or cars, drugs such as cocaine or marijuana have no legal market because the use and sale of these drugs are strictly prohibited under the law. In order to uphold this policy of drug prohibition, America spends billions of dollars each year to stop illegal drugs from entering the country. The nation employs thousands of border guards, police officers, judges, prison staff, and other agents to help fight a "war on drugs," and enforce increasingly tougher drug laws that mandate zero tolerance for illegal drug use and no leniency for those caught using or selling drugs. U.S. courts and prisons are overcrowded with people who have disobeyed these laws. Some have

An armed DEA officer stands guard over hundreds of kilos of cocaine and firearms seized during a raid of a Miami drug lord's home.

committed violent, drug-related crimes, but others are guilty only of possessing an illegal substance. Many of the tactics used to enforce the nation's drug laws, such as drug testing at schools and workplaces, and searches and seizures of money, cars, and houses where drugs are found, raise questions about personal liberties and the right to privacy. These tactics also give rise to perceptions among many of the nation's minority groups that the drug laws unfairly target and punish them, since they are more likely than white Americans to be arrested, go to jail, and receive long prison sentences for possessing or selling drugs.

Despite the enormous amount of money and the number of resources and lives the nation devotes to stopping the illegal drug trade, demand for illegal drugs is greater in the United States than anywhere else in the world. Some people say the war on drugs is worth the effort since it is the only way to stop illegal drugs from destroying lives, families, and neighborhoods, and corrupting young people. They argue that drug use is immoral and must not be tolerated under any circumstances. Supporters of current U.S. policies point to evidence that the use of some illegal drugs has declined since the 1980s when America began to pass strict laws and crack down on drug use through tougher law enforcement.

Should the Drug Laws Be Changed?

There are also many Americans, however, who believe that the dollars, lives, and liberties lost in the war on drugs are too high a price to pay. They question whether current prohibition policies are working and seek ways to reform drug laws. Most people seek moderate changes, such as reducing the harsh penalties for possessing small amounts of illegal drugs so that a young person found with a bag of cocaine does not serve a sentence out of proportion to his crime, or allowing patients with cancer or AIDS to gain legal access to marijuana to ease their pain.

Among those who seek reform, a small but vocal minority would like to overturn the laws prohibiting drugs completely and make marijuana, cocaine, and other drugs legally available for use and sale. The idea of legalizing drugs is highly controversial, supported by roughly 15 percent of U.S. residents who have very different visions about how such a policy would be carried out. Legalization was once easily dismissed as the domain of drug enthusiasts, reggae music stars, and libertarians, who believe in drastically reducing government interference in people's lives. But as more Americans have grown disillusioned with harsh laws and policies that have failed to significantly reduce drug use, they too have joined the call to legalize drugs. Today's legalization supporters come from all walks of life. They are civil rights activists, police officers, judges, business leaders, medical doctors, local politicians, and average Americans whose brothers, sisters, husbands, wives, and children have suffered under the country's zero tolerance drug laws. In recent years, as this diverse group of legalization supporters speak out about the need to reform the drug laws, more Americans have begun to pay attention.

1

Illegal Drug Use in America

A SUCCESSFUL BUSINESSMAN slips a coworker a one hundred dollar bill in exchange for a small bag of powder cocaine. A group of college students smoke and share marijuana in the hallway of their dormitory. A young mother sits on the sofa of a low-income apartment building, inhaling the fumes from a rock of crack cocaine while several children play in the room next door. And white middle-class youth in the Midwest "cook" methamphetamine in a suburban garage before heading out to a late night party. Illegal drug use in America has many different faces. The media often focuses on drugs in stories about crime and the inner city, but drug users belong to every race and social class. They live in densely populated cities, small factory and farming towns, and suburban housing projects across the country.

These different types of drug users may have vastly different drug use experiences, depending on their backgrounds, where they live, and the reasons they turn to drugs in the first place. A casual drug user looking for a weekend high shares little in common with a heroin addict whose entire life revolves around getting his or her next drug fix. In recent years, political leaders, including several presidential candidates, have admitted that they tried drugs such as marijuana in their youth, yet they have gone on to seek national office and lead prominent, successful lives. In contrast, in poor inner-city neighborhoods, drug use takes a much higher toll and drug users get fewer second chances. In these communities, heavy

Drug use affects all segments of society. Here, recovering addicts participate in Hands Across the Bridge, an annual event celebrating their ongoing efforts to stay clean.

drug use often leads to crime, homelessness, violence, and a life spent in and out of prison.

In order to consider what would happen to American society if drugs such as heroin or marijuana became legally available, it is important to know who uses illegal drugs under current laws, which drugs they use, and why they use them.

Defining Illegal Drugs

A drug is a natural substance or man-made chemical that can be used to control or prevent physical or psychological ailments, change the way the body works, and alter mood or behavior. In the United States, some drugs are sold over the counter as medicines in pharmacies and stores. Others are available only with a doctor's prescription. Still others are forbidden under almost any circumstances. (The word *narcotics* is often used interchangeably with "illegal drugs," although it actually refers only to opium and related substances.) In 1970, the U.S. Congress passed the Controlled Substances Act (or CSA), which combined the nation's many existing laws about drug use into a single comprehensive federal law. This law governs the use of all drugs that have the potential for abuse, defined as using a drug in a harmful way that causes the user to lose control, or dependence, defined as physical or psychological reliance on a drug. Users who become dependent suffer withdrawal symptoms, such as tremors or anxiety, if they stop using drugs.

The aim of the CSA is to make sure that potentially dangerous drugs are used under safe conditions for legitimate medical purposes only. It requires that drugs be placed into one of five schedules, or categories, based on scientific evaluations of how likely they are to lead to abuse and dependence. Drugs that are placed in Schedule I are considered to have the highest potential for abuse and no accepted medical use. These drugs, including heroin, LSD, and marijuana, are subject to almost total prohibition except in tightly controlled research situations. Doctors may not prescribe these drugs and they are not legally available for sale anywhere in the country. Schedule II drugs, including cocaine and morphine, are also tightly controlled, but are made available under specific medical conditions such as controlling pain during surgery under a doctor's supervision. Schedule III and IV drugs are viewed as slightly less dangerous, and include barbiturates that are sometimes prescribed to reduce anxiety or help people sleep, and performance- or body-enhancing anabolic steroids. Schedule V drugs, considered to have the least potential for abuse, include common cold and cough medicines sold over the counter in drugstores.

This system of categorizing drugs may seem straightforward, but it is complicated by the fact that the schedules must be constantly reviewed and changed as new drugs become popular among illegal users, and new scientific information emerges about drugs already listed in the schedules. Political or social factors also influence the scheduling decisions. For example, government officials are often concerned that if a popular illegal drug is approved for medical use, this may downplay its dangers and encourage more people to try it recreationally.

By far the most controversial government decision on drug scheduling is the placement of marijuana in Schedule I alongside hard drugs such as heroin and LSD. The status of marijuana has remained unchanged since 1970 despite the lack of firm scientific evidence that it causes physical dependence or severe withdrawal symptoms. In recent years, studies have also shown that smoking marijuana may help relieve the pain caused by diseases such as glaucoma (which creates pressure on the eyes and leads to vision loss), cancer, and AIDS. So far, government officials have resisted placing marijuana into a less restrictive schedule, because they fear such a decision would send the wrong message and undermine years of prevention and education efforts that have attempted to discourage young people from trying marijuana.

Schedule of Controlled Substances

Rating	Examples	Characteristics
Schedule I	· Heroin · Mescaline · LSD · MDMA (Ecstasy) · Marijuana · PCP · GHB · Methaqualone · Psilocybin (mushrooms)	High potential for abuse; no currently accepted medical use in the United States.
Schedule II	· Opium and Opiates · Methamphetamines · Demerol · Percodan · Cocaine · Amphetamines · Oxycodone · Hydrocodone	High potential for abuse; currently accepted medical use with severe restrictions.
Schedule III	· Anabolic steroids · Codeine · Certain barbiturates · Ketamine (Special K)	Potential for abuse, but less than Schedule I and II substances; currently accepted medical use.
Schedule IV	· Certain barbiturates · Benzodiazepines (Sleeping pills)	Less potential for abuse; available by prescription.
Schedule V	· Cold and cough medicines	Least potential for abuse; available over the counter.

Illegal Drug Use in the United States: How Widespread Is It?

There is no way to know for certain how many Americans use illegal drugs. Statistics on drug use are hard to pin down. The only way to find out about people's drug use is to ask them directly. But those who admit that they take illegal drugs are guilty of committing a crime and immoral in the eyes of many Americans. People who respond to drug surveys may not answer truthfully because they are afraid that their answers will not be kept confidential, that they will face punishment, or that their friends and family might find out and disapprove of their drug use. On the other hand, teenagers and other young people may even exaggerate their drug use to fit in with their peers.

The most widely used survey on illegal drug use in the United States is the government-sponsored "National Survey on Drug Use and Health," or NSDUH, which is based on interviews with people who represent a large cross section of the U.S. population. NSDUH first began tracking

In Boston, a young woman rides on the hands of a crowd of people participating in a rally for the legalization of marijuana, classified as a Schedule I controlled substance.

drug use in America in 1971 (when it was called the National Household Survey on Drug Abuse). In 2003, survey workers conducted more than sixty-seven thousand interviews with U.S. residents in houses, apartments, homeless shelters, military bases, and college dormitories across the nation. Respondents were asked questions about whether they have used drugs such as marijuana and cocaine, how often they have used them, where they obtained the drugs, and how they perceived the risks of using them. They were also asked background questions about their education, mental health, employment, and race or ethnicity.

The 2003 NSDUH reveals that an estimated 19.5 million Americans or 8.2 percent of the population aged twelve and older are current illicit drug users (defined as someone who used an illicit drug one or more times in the month prior to the survey). More than 12 percent of respondents used an illicit drug in the past year, and 41.7 percent reported some use of an illicit drug at least once during their lifetime. Put in slightly different terms, this means that more than four out of every ten Americans have disobeyed the laws prohibiting drug use at some point in their lives.

Who Uses Illegal Drugs?

The 2003 NSDUH also confirms that current (past month) drug users are a very diverse group, but that there are some traits they often have in common. Most current users are in their teens to early thirties. They include more men than women, with the gender difference most striking among those who use drugs every day. Men far outnumber women among regular, daily users. There is also a close link between current drug use and educational status. American high school students who do not plan to attend college are more likely to be current or regular users of illegal drugs than those who are college bound. This is despite the fact that many college graduates report having sometime tried an illegal drug.

Among the racial and ethnic groups in the United States, media accounts about drug use often focus on low-income African Americans and Latinos. This is because the rate of drug selling and imprisonment for drug-related offenses among young black and Latino males is disproportionately high. But these accounts can be misleading. The NSDUH shows that the rate of current drug use among whites, African Americans, and Latinos in the United States is very similar (within one percentage point).

Statistics on hard-drug users and addicts are especially difficult to obtain, since these populations are unlikely to respond to surveys, but the NSDUH does track some of the circumstances that make a person more likely to become a regular or heavy drug user. Adults who were unemployed at the time of the survey, for example, were more likely to report current drug use than those with full-time jobs. Serious mental illness among adults reporting regular drug use was also high. Dr. John Morgan, a drug policy expert at the City College of New York, confirms that the people who "lose it to drugs are overwhelmingly people who have very

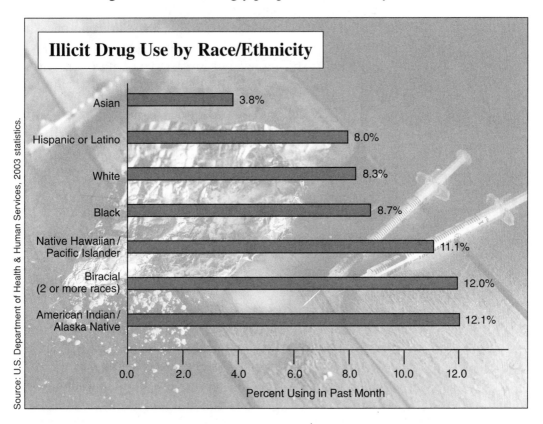

Illicit Drug Use by Race/Ethnicity

Source: U.S. Department of Health & Human Services, 2003 statistics.

little at stake, very little hope,"[2] including those who suffer from poverty or mental illness, or who lack supportive families and prospects for the future.

Drug Use Among Young People

One fact that has remained constant over the years is that illegal drug use in America is closely linked to youth. Most adult users first experiment with drugs in high school or college. The drug epidemic of the 1960s and 1970s began on the nation's college campuses and spread downward in age. Drugs, especially marijuana and LSD, were closely tied to the popular culture, from music and movies to fashion. Young people who considered themselves part of a counterculture listened to songs by groups such as the Beatles and the Rolling Stones that glorified smoking marijuana, getting stoned, and "tripping" on LSD. They wore T-shirts and pennants emblazoned with images of marijuana leaves. Illegal drug use among young people reached its peak in 1979, but even today, the authors of one national survey point out, "It is still true that this nation's secondary school students and young adults show a level of involvement with illicit drugs that is as great as has been documented in any other industrialized nation in the world."[3]

Drugs of all types tend to be easiest to find in schools, colleges, and other places where large groups of young people gather. In part, this is because young people are more likely than other members of the population to engage in risky behaviors and to rebel against the social norms established by parents and other adults. Young people are also heavily influenced by their peers. If their friends or acquaintances are using drugs, they too are likely to be introduced to drugs, often at a party or other social event.

A second nationwide survey, called Monitoring the Future (or MTF), focuses solely on drug use by young people. Each year, the MTF survey is administered by staff from the University of Michigan in more than 120 high schools across the country. High school seniors, as well as eighth and tenth graders, answer questions about their use of a wide range of drugs, how difficult or easy it is to ac-

cess these drugs, and how they perceive the risks of using them.

On the 2003 MTF survey, slightly more than half of all high school seniors (51 percent) reported any illicit drug use at some time in their lives. Close to 12 percent, or one in every eight seniors, reported current (past month) use of illegal drugs in 2002. The MTF survey makes it clear that many drugs are readily available to young people. More than half of students aged twelve to seventeen say that it would be fairly easy or very easy to obtain marijuana if they wanted some.

MTF also tracks behaviors and attitudes that might cause people to abuse or become dependent on drugs at an early age. As in the general population, young drug abusers are at higher risk than their peers for serious mental health problems, including depression, behavior problems, personality disorders, and suicidal thoughts. They are more likely to be delinquent and face arrest or intervention by the juvenile justice system. In contrast, those who have positive attitudes toward school, feel their assigned school work is meaningful, or that the things they learn in school will become important later in life, are less likely to have used illicit drugs at an early age.

This teenage methamphetamine addict is struggling to regain control of her life as she fights to break her addiction. Drug users typically start at a young age.

Trends in Illegal Drug Use

Cocaine, heroin, Oxycontin, LSD, ketamine, and Ecstasy are among the long list of illegal drugs that are used and abused in America by young people and others to alter mood and consciousness. In any given year, some drugs may gain in popularity while others fade. "One of the dynamics that keeps the drug epidemic rolling," say the authors of the MTF survey, "is the emergence of new drugs whose hazards are little known."[4] In the late 1990s, for example, the drug Ecstasy, or MDMA, suddenly appeared on the club scene. Ecstasy produces a feeling of euphoria and well-being that can last through the night. (It also increases body temperature and may cause changes in the brain with repeated use.) Word of Ecstasy's effects quickly spread among young people who attend nightclubs and "rave" parties through Internet chat rooms and message boards. Within only a few years,

In 2002 DEA chief Asa Hutchinson displays a map detailing Ecstasy trafficking routes. Ecstasy remains one of the most popular illicit drugs among young adults.

Ecstasy became one of the most widely used drugs among young adults across the nation.

Another drug that has spread rapidly among young users in recent years is methamphetamine. Meth is a highly addictive drug that is sometimes known as "the poor man's cocaine" because its initial effects are similar to cocaine and it has become popular among working-class whites and young people in many regions of the West and Midwest. The increasing use of meth is alarming to U.S. drug officials because it can be made cheaply using common, highly toxic household chemicals, as well as ingredients easy to find in cold remedies and diet pills.

In addition to the continuous flow of new drugs such as Ecstasy and meth, old drugs often reemerge among illegal users in a new, less expensive, or easier to use form. The MTF authors attribute this to a process they call "generational forgetting." They explain that when one generation of young people replaces another and has no direct experience with the effects or dangers of certain drugs, this can "set the stage for a whole new epidemic of use."[5] One example of this was an upsurge in heroin use among young people in the 1990s when a purer form of the drug become available that could be smoked or snorted rather than injected. Young people who might have been afraid to inject themselves with a needle, especially since using shared or dirty needles increases their risk of contracting AIDS and other diseases, were more willing to experiment with heroin in this newer, smokable form.

In fact, for young people and others seeking a drug-induced high, the number of existing drugs and products that can be reinvented or diverted for recreational use seems endless. Law enforcement officials are constantly forced to play catch up as they try to anticipate and rein in the next illegal drug trend. This is the case with many common prescription drugs that have been discovered by illegal users for something other than their recommended medical use. In 2003, an estimated 6.3 million Americans reported current use of prescription drugs for nonmedical purposes. Among these drugs, Ritalin, which is used to control the symptoms of hyperactivity and attention deficit disorder (ADD), and Oxycontin, a painkiller that is often viewed as a substitute for heroin, were among the most widely reported drugs used by high school students in the late 1990s. Despite tight controls over these prescription drugs, they are often diverted from pharmacies and doctors' offices by illegal means, including theft, forged prescriptions, bribery of health professionals, and "doctor shopping" in which people who may or may not have legitimate illnesses visit many doctors to acquire large amounts of these drugs and then resell them.

Marijuana, Cocaine, and Heroin

Yet even as other drugs go in and out of fashion, since the 1960s, marijuana has remained by far the most commonly used illegal drug in America. One out of every three Americans over the age of twelve, or more than 90 million people, have tried marijuana at least once in their lives. In 2003, roughly 14.6 million people aged twelve and older were current marijuana users. Marijuana is derived from the flowers and leaves of the cannabis (or hemp) plant, and its potent psychoactive, or mind-altering ingredient, is called THC. In recent years, the number of young people who say they disapprove of marijuana use is up sharply, which some attribute to a successful media and prevention campaign warning of marijuana's dangers. Nevertheless, there were still more than 2 million Americans who began using marijuana for the first time in 2002 alone.

By comparison, the number of people who use illegal drugs such as cocaine and heroin is far lower. Although as many as 34 million Americans have probably experimented with cocaine in some form since it regained popularity in the 1970s, only an estimated 2 to 3 million today are regular cocaine users. Roughly six hundred thousand of these users are dependent on crack, a cheaper, more potent form of cocaine. Both powder cocaine and crack are extracted from leaves of the coca plant that grows in the Andes Mountains of South America. Crack is mixed with baking soda and sold in smokable rocks that are quicker to reach the bloodstream and produce an intense high. It is sold so cheaply and its effects are so short-lived, that people need to use it again and again in a single day. Following the arrival of crack on the scene in the 1980s, newspaper and television reports were filled with stories about burned-out addicts in inner-city neighborhoods, babies born addicted to the drug, and violent shootings between rival drug gangs over crack sales. Widespread use of crack in the 1980s left a small population of heavy users, many of them poor African Americans and Latinos who remain physically dependent on the drug. But by the late 1990s, word had spread about the dangers of crack use, and relatively few people in recent years began trying crack for the first time.

The number of current heroin users in the nation is even smaller. There are estimated to be somewhere close to 750,000 regular, heavy heroin users. And there are good reasons for this. Heroin is processed from morphine, a substance derived from the raw opium found in the seedpods of

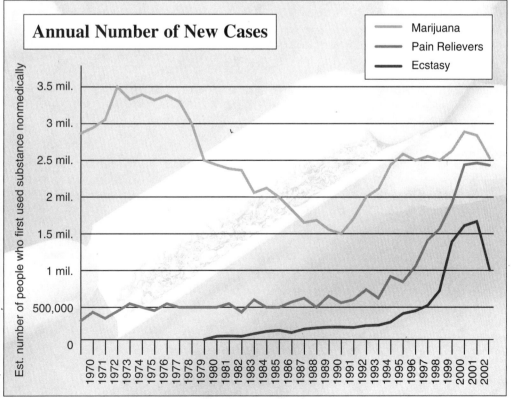

Source: 2003 National Survey on Drug Use and Health, September 2004, Substance Abuse and Mental Health Services Administration.

the opium poppy plant. It is a notoriously dangerous, highly addictive drug that is associated in the public mind with the down-and-out addict and track marks across his or her veins from repeated injections with a needle. Today's heroin addicts, however, are also likely to be white middle-class teenagers, living in the suburbs, who snort or smoke the drug.

Yet most American young people perceive the use of hard or addictive drugs such as heroin and crack as dangerous. The vast majority disapproves of using or even experimenting with such drugs, and these attitudes have not changed much over the past two decades. Many lawmakers and members of the American public of all ages agree. They not only disapprove of heroin and other hard drugs, but also believe that those who become abusers and addicts should be punished.

2

Why Are Drugs Illegal?

ON SEPTEMBER 5, 1989, President George H.W. Bush appeared on national television to announce his plan for achieving "victory over drugs." He held up to the cameras a plastic bag of crack cocaine that had been seized a few days earlier in a park across the street from the White House and declared that its contents were "turning our cities into battle zones and murdering our children."[6]

For several years leading up to the president's speech, stories about a crack cocaine epidemic filled the national airwaves and newspapers. Each week brought shocking new accounts of burned-out drug addicts and gang members caught up in violent gunfights over drug sales in the inner cities. These stories confirmed Americans' long-held beliefs that drugs were linked to many of the worst ills of society, including high crime rates, delinquency, immorality, child abuse, violence, and a rejection of traditional family values. Political leaders responded with vows to step up the war on drugs, the government's efforts to rid the nation of illegal drugs. They declared zero tolerance for illegal drugs and passed the harshest drug laws in United States history with tough mandatory penalties for drug users and sellers. Most of these laws remain in place as of 2005.

Close to 85 percent of Americans continue to believe that drugs such as cocaine, marijuana, and heroin should remain illegal. Often their views are heavily influenced by religious and moral beliefs. When politicians or public figures suggest

In 1989 former president George H.W. Bush displays a bag of crack cocaine during a televised speech to the American people detailing his plan for achieving victory in the war on drugs.

that the government reexamine its laws about illegal drugs, they risk serious damage to their careers. As one former legal adviser to Congress put it in 1999, "no member of Congress is going to lose a vote because they're tough on drugs."[7] The nation's policy of drug prohibition is rarely challenged, because it is based on widely held attitudes and assumptions about why drugs must remain illegal.

A Brief History

The first laws against illegal drug use date back to the early part of the twentieth century. Before that time, drugs such as cocaine and opium were widely available and used. Doctors prescribed opiates (derived from the poppy plant) for a range of ailments, including pain, sleeplessness, and anxiety. Patients could obtain drugs from their doctors or buy them as home remedies. Opium, imported from China, was the first drug to become widely popular for recreational use. The euphoric effects of cocaine also made it an especially popular ingredient in everything from medicines and wines to ointments. The original formula for Coca Cola, like other popular drinks of the late nineteenth and early twentieth centuries, contained a significant amount of cocaine. By the turn of the twentieth century, the easy availability of these drugs had created a population of addicts estimated at 250,000 people. As the number of addicts grew, so too did public awareness and fear of drug abuse, which was associated with criminals, prostitutes, gamblers, and others who were seen as living immoral, pleasure-seeking lifestyles. This fear was heightened whenever drugs became linked to minority racial and ethnic groups that were deeply distrusted by many white Americans. When cocaine use, for example, began to spread from middle-class whites to poor blacks in the South, white Southerners were afraid its use would cause blacks to rise up against them. Stories began to circulate that cocaine granted blacks superhuman powers, even enabling them to withstand bullets that could kill an ordinary person.

Yet it was not until the 1960s, at a time of political and social unrest, that the illegal drug problem first captured the public's attention on a large scale. With the post–World War II baby boom, there were more young people in America than in earlier years. Many of them began smoking marijuana and experimenting with drugs such as heroin and LSD. Soldiers fighting an increasingly unpopular war in Vietnam also gained access to locally grown marijuana and a pure form of heroin that left many of them chemically dependent on drugs when they returned. Some older Americans were shocked by the behavior and attitudes of the young baby boom generation. They viewed rampant drug use as a rejection of patriotism and other traditional values. In 1970, Richard Nixon was elected president on a platform of restoring law and order to the country. He declared a "total war on dangerous drugs" and vowed to hunt drug traffickers "to the end of the earth."[8]

In the 1980s, the nation began to devote more energy, resources, and manpower to the war on drugs than ever before. Fueled by the highly publicized cocaine overdose deaths of celebrities such as *Saturday Night Live* comedian John Belushi and college basketball star and NBA draft pick Len Bias, and the rise of crack and related gun violence in the inner cities, the drug war took on a new sense of urgency. The American public was ready to believe almost anything about the evils of drug use. Media accounts from these years were sensationalistic and often inaccurate. *Reader's Digest,* for example, took out ads in many major newspapers with the

An advocate for LSD, Dr. Timothy Leary (center) encouraged young people in the 1960s to reject societal conventions and ingest large quantities of the hallucinogen.

headline, "From Middle America Come Reports of Teen Parties Where Cocaine is Sprinkled on the Popcorn."[9] Yet few drug users would be likely to waste cocaine in this way because of its high price and the fact that this would ruin the drug's effects and make the popcorn taste terrible. Meanwhile, lawmakers tried to outdo each other as they proposed tougher drug laws and massive new expenditures to fight the war on drugs. In 1989, shortly after President Bush's appearance on television with the bag of crack, 64 percent of those responding to a *New York Times*/CBS news poll said that they believed drugs were now "the most important problem facing this country today."[10]

Drugs Are Dangerous

One of the main reasons that drugs are illegal is that they can cause grave danger to the health and well-being of people who use them. Laws banning illegal drug use are not unlike other so-called paternalistic laws that protect American citizens from harm. These include regulations about the use of seat belts and bicycle helmets, as well as laws prohibiting people from jaywalking or committing suicide. When drugs are ingested often enough or in large enough quantities, they interfere with the normal functioning of the body and brain. Drugs such as LSD, for example, slow reaction times and affect users' ability to avoid risky situations, especially when they are driving a car or operating other heavy machinery. Others, such as cocaine, reduce people's inhibitions and increase the likelihood that they will make impulsive decisions that endanger their health or well-being. Heavy users of hard drugs such as heroin often suffer severe physical and psychological distress if they stop taking the drug. Heroin produces a dangerous chemical dependence that leaves its users obsessively fixated on getting more heroin. Habitual crack users are driven by the need to recapture the feeling of their last drug-induced high. As the intense, euphoric effects of crack wear off, users experience a crash that leaves them depressed and anxious. Heavy users may even reach a point where they can no longer remain productive members of society. They neglect their own basic health and hygiene and are unable to hold down a job or support themselves financially. Many end up homeless and on the street.

In addition to these direct health risks, there are also dangers associated with the methods and equipment people use to ingest drugs. Intravenous users who share needles, for example, are often exposed to serious and potentially lethal diseases such as HIV/AIDS and hepatitis (a virus that infects the liver). The "cooking" of methamphetamine in homegrown labs is a dangerous process that involves highly flammable and corrosive household products, such as paint thinner, battery acid, and rubbing alcohol. U.S. law enforcement officers discover many meth labs as a result of an explosion or fire that causes extensive property damage and death.

Yet laws against illegal drugs are different than paternalistic laws that require people to wear seat belts or bicycle helmets to prevent injury, because there are many ways in which drug users inflict harm on other people, not just themselves. In an intoxicated state, users of some drugs may become violent and aggressive and act in ways that threaten family members or others around them. Those who use PCP, anabolic steroids (used to increase muscle strength), and methamphetamine, for example, are more likely to commit physical assault, rape, and vandalism. Intravenous users who share needles expose other IV users to diseases such as AIDS and hepatitis. They also put their sexual partners, health care providers, and nursing or unborn children at great risk for contracting these diseases, and hasten its spread among the general public. The nearly 11 million Americans who reported driving under the influence of illegal drugs in 2003 risked not only their own lives, but also those of their passengers and other drivers. Perhaps the most innocent victims of drug abuse are newborn babies whose mothers take drugs during their pregnancies. Each year, an estimated five hundred thousand babies in the United States are born prenatally exposed to illegal drugs, alcohol, and tobacco. Of the children who survive regular drug use during pregnancy, many suffer physical damage,

Police investigators in California examine the rubble of a methamphetamine lab after it exploded in flames. Preparing meth involves highly flammable chemicals.

retardation, and learning disabilities that will affect them for the rest of their lives.

Protecting America's Children

Children of all ages are often the innocent victims of drug abuse. The idea of protecting children from drugs has proved to be one of the most powerful and persuasive arguments for boosting antidrug expenditures and passing tougher drug laws. Politicians often declare that drug laws and policies—from longer prison sentences for drug users to mandatory drug testing in the schools—are in children's best interest. Child psychiatrist and author Robert Coles says children "need the societal order to say we stand for something. . . . We're just finally beginning to recognize what it means to use cigarettes, and to turn around and say it's all right to use heroin and marijuana is wrong."[11]

Drugs are associated with many social problems that affect children directly, including broken homes, family violence, and child abuse. The vast majority of child abuse cases nationwide involve a parent with a drug or alcohol problem. In the inner-city neighborhoods hit hardest by crack and heroin abuse, children are often forced to grow up amidst desperate poverty and neglect. Some of the most disturbing media accounts of crack abuse involve children playing in vacant lots littered with empty crack vials or forced to sell drugs to earn extra income for the family. Children whose parents are drug abusers are at high risk for becoming sick,

A longtime user and dealer shows her young son the correct way to deal drugs on the street by keeping hold of the bag until payment is received.

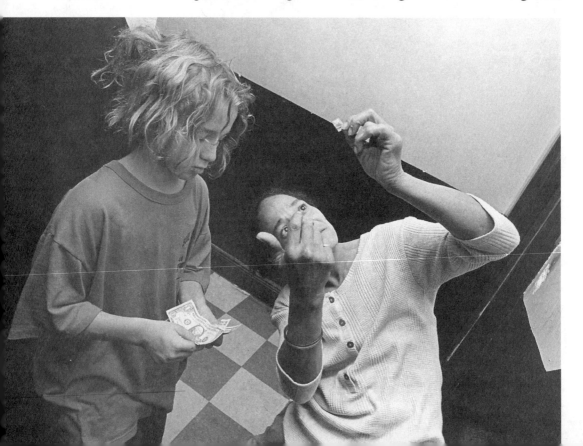

dropping out of school, being placed in foster care, or becoming drug abusers themselves. In the 1980s, crack addiction was linked to a tripling in the number of reported cases in New York City in which parents abused or neglected their children. Foster care placements during these years jumped dramatically. And the problem is not limited to cocaine or heroin. In recent years, the rise of methamphetamine in many regions of the country has also taken a heavy toll on children. Children raised in houses where meth labs are present are more likely to be physically and sexually abused by family members and others in the house, or left neglected and hungry while their parents fall into a deep meth-induced sleep for days after withdrawing from the drug.

Drugs are also blamed for corrupting young people by leading them into a life of immoral, reckless behavior. Teenagers who experiment with drugs are more likely to skip school, perform poorly in class, and engage in risky behaviors, such as driving under the influence of drugs. Those who live in poverty-stricken urban areas with an entrenched drug culture, sometimes become *mules* (messengers) and lookouts for neighborhood drug dealers. Hundreds of young lives have been lost in these inner-city, mainly minority neighborhoods in the gunfire between rival drug gangs.

Some people view young drug users and sellers as innocent victims. Many legalization proponents, for example, argue that if the nation were serious about promoting children's welfare, the laws would focus less on punishment and more on treatment and support. This is the view of law professor Douglas Husak, who writes, "When a child is caught with drugs, sympathies are put aside and mercy is seldom forthcoming." [12]

Others, however, perceive young drug users as dropouts and criminals who threaten the moral fabric of the nation. In the 1970s, marijuana was blamed for turning a generation of young people into wasted dropouts, unproductive and lacking in ambition. In the 1980s, a very different image took hold of the young, typically minority dealers and users who were caught up in the cocaine trade. They were perceived as frightening, violent predators who lacked the ability to distinguish right from wrong. William Bennett, former "drug czar" or director of national drug policy under the first Bush administration, painted a frightening portrait of these mainly black youths caught up in a life of drugs and crime. He called them a generation of juvenile "super-predators" who "murder, assault, rape, rob, burglarize, deal deadly drugs, join gun-toting gangs, and create serious communal disorders."[13]

Drugs Are Linked to Crime

Those who favor a strict ban on illegal drugs say not only is such a ban in the best interest of children, but it is also the most effective way of preserving law and order and reducing crime. The connection between drugs and crime is so strong, that politicians who challenge the drug laws are often accused of being "soft on crime," a charge that can quickly spell the end of a political career. The fear of being labeled soft on crime prevents even those who may have private concerns about the nation's tough drug laws from expressing themselves publicly. The police chief of one Texas county echoed the sentiments of many Americans when he testified to Congress against drug legalization in 1999: "If those who favor legalization have their way, our efforts to reduce crime and protect our children from the horrors of drug abuse will be wasted. It is a simple fact; increased drug abuse and increased crime go hand in hand."[14]

For many Americans, the link between drugs and crime first became cause for alarm at the height of the crack epidemic in the 1980s. Major cities across the nation, including Detroit, Chicago, New York, Miami, and Los Angeles, witnessed a dramatic rise in assaults, robberies, and murders. For several years, drug crimes remained highly visible on the nation's front pages and nightly newscasts. Author and drug policy analyst Mark Kleiman describes the image of the urban crack dealer that filled the public with fear at this time, "with his beeper, his hundred-dollar sneakers, his assault rifle, and his willingness to use it on rivals and random passersby."[15] By 1990, between 50 and 60 percent of all those arrested in the nation's largest cities tested positive for cocaine or crack, regardless of the crime they were charged with at the time of arrest.

Heavy users of hard drugs such as cocaine or amphetamine rank high among the most serious and active criminals in the nation. In a recent government survey of victims of violent crimes, including rape, physical assault, and domestic violence, one-third reported that they believed their assailants were under the influence of drugs or alcohol at the time they committed their crimes. Heavy drug users also account for a large portion of the nation's theft and property crime. Heroin and cocaine fetch a very high price on the street. Some compulsive users will resort to any desperate measures to satisfy their next drug fix, including stealing, identity theft (stealing credit cards or bank account numbers), prostitution, and drug dealing.

Los Angeles police frisk suspected gang members for drugs and weapons in 1985. Critics of legalization maintain that drug use is intimately linked to crime rates.

Drug Use Is Immoral

Yet for many Americans, the most compelling reason for making drugs illegal is that drug use is immoral. People

who hold this view do not distinguish between so-called soft drugs, such as marijuana, and hard drugs, such as heroin. Instead, they assume, based on fundamental religious or personal beliefs, that all drug use is wrong. They perceive the desire to get high or seek altered states of consciousness as a sign of moral weakness, and associate widespread drug use with periods in American history when traditional values were under attack, including the 1960s and 1970s when marijuana became a symbol of lax social attitudes and countercultural rebellion. "Drug use is wrong because it is immoral and it is immoral because it enslaves the mind and destroys the soul," [16] writes social critic James Q. Wilson.

Unable to turn to the police for protection, this crack addict and dealer finds herself at the mercy of her supplier after she smoked the drugs she was meant to sell.

The moral argument for a ban on drugs assumes that it is possible and desirable to legislate morality. Those who make this argument believe that one of the functions of law is to uphold the nation's moral principles and express disapproval of an activity that is wrong, even if this conflicts with personal liberties. They often argue that the most effective way to reform drug users is with the threat of punishment and jail time. Former New York City mayor and prosecutor Rudolph Giuliani suggests, "The law is a teaching instrument among other things. You can't say drugs are bad at the same time that you are making them legal." [17]

3

The War on Drugs and Its Costs

FROM HIS BASE in the South American country of Colombia, the notorious drug lord Pablo Escobar and his Medellín drug cartel (business monopoly formed when independent groups join together) controlled 80 percent of the cocaine that entered the United States for much of the 1980s. Escobar was one of the wealthiest men in the world, living a lavish lifestyle that included mansions, his own private island, heliports, swimming pools, and a private zoo. He was also a ruthless killer who was responsible for the murders of half of Colombia's supreme court justices, journalists, soldiers, policemen, a presidential candidate, and hundreds of innocent civilians.

Under the first Bush administration, the United States began supplying millions of dollars, training, equipment, and Special Forces to aid Colombian soldiers in their efforts to hunt Escobar down. In December 1993, this massive U.S.-backed manhunt finally paid off when Escobar was killed in a hail of bullets from Colombian police. The U.S. government applauded the downfall of one of the world's most violent criminals. Yet within months of his death, a rival Colombian drug cartel rose to take his place. Despite the hugely expensive effort to bring down Escobar, his removal had little long-term effect on the supply of cocaine entering the United States.

Each year, the nation spends billions of dollars in an attempt to crack down and punish drug users and suppliers. The government has passed zero tolerance drug laws that mandate longer prison sentences for drug users and sellers, and has stepped up patrols at the borders to prevent drugs from entering the country. Despite these efforts, drug suppliers still find ways to avoid detection and ensure their products get to market. The goal of U.S. drug policy is to reduce drug use and eventually, to create a "Drug-Free America," but supporters of legalization say that the war on illegal drugs costs the nation too much. They ask how much longer the government can continue to pursue policies that have failed to significantly reduce U.S. demand for drugs or the number of suppliers around the world who are eager to satisfy it.

Pablo Escobar is shown here with his bodyguard in Medellín, Colombia, in 1983. After his death in 1993, a new drug cartel emerged to supply cocaine to the United States.

During a 2002 press conference, President George W. Bush holds up a report that outlines his new strategy in the continuing war on drugs.

Weighing the Costs of the Drug War

Every American taxpayer helps to fund the war on illegal drugs. The federal government spends more than $19 billion per year directly fighting the drug war. State and local governments spend almost another $18 billion per year. Close to two-thirds of the federal drug control money is devoted to law enforcement, which includes policing, arresting, and punishing drug dealers and users, stepped up border patrols, eradicating (destroying) drug crops through aerial spraying, and other efforts to interrupt the supply of drugs entering the country. The remaining one-third is split between treatment and prevention programs, including media campaigns warning against drug use and funding for drug testing programs in schools.

Despite this large taxpayer investment, there is little pressure on the government to prove that drug control programs are working. This is because most politicians and many members of the American public believe that drug offenders get the punishment they deserve. The nation punishes and imprisons rapists, they say, without having to prove that it is cost effective. Critics, on the other hand, insist that the government should be held accountable for the increasing expenditures it devotes to drug enforcement. "The trend," says drug policy analyst Kleiman, "is toward more and more extreme efforts with less and less clarity about why they are undertaken or what benefits they are expected to produce."[18]

Increased law enforcement and pressure on drug suppliers and dealers is meant to reduce drug use by making drugs more expensive and harder to find. Yet drug policy analysts Peter Reuter and Robert MacCoun, consultants with the nonprofit research group, the Rand Corporation, observe just the opposite. They tracked the street prices of cocaine and heroin since the early 1980s when the nation began to intensify its efforts to cut off drug supply and enforce tough policies, such as stepped up arrests and longer prison sentences. What they found is that the prices of these drugs have actually fallen steadily. Reuter and MacCoun are unable to point to any obvious reason for a drop in prices since demand for cocaine and heroin has not changed much among regular, heavy users and supply has also remained steady. Yet they suggest that high level arrests and enforcement have clearly failed to raise prices or make these drugs harder to find. For example, the percentage of high school seniors reporting on the MTF survey that cocaine was "available" or "readily available" was higher in 1989 (55 percent) than in 1980 (30 percent) despite the passage of tough drug laws and harsher punishments. Legalization proponents such as Husak say the statistics are "sobering." "Hundreds of billions of dollars on law enforcement expended over dozens of years have not had an obvious impact on the demand for illicit drugs or the difficulty of obtaining them."[19]

Zero Tolerance Drug Policies

The huge expenditures on law enforcement are part of a federal policy that mandates zero tolerance for illegal drugs under any circumstances, and no leniency for those caught using or selling them. "Zero tolerance" first became official government policy at the height of the cocaine scare in the 1980s. In 1986, Congress passed the Anti-Drug bill, which boosted the penalties for federal drug offenses by lengthening prison time, eliminating the possibility of parole (early release) in most drug cases, and establishing mandatory minimum sentences for those convicted of violating drug laws. With mandatory minimums, Congress dictates to federal judges across the country the minimum jail time convicted drug offenders must receive for certain crimes based on the type of drug in the case, the amount involved, and whether firearms were present. For example, first time offenders convicted of possession with intent to distribute five grams of crack cocaine (one gram is roughly equal to a single packet of sweetener) receive a five-year prison sentence with no possibility of parole. This is true regardless of a person's role in the crime or how dangerous they are to the community.

Mandatory minimum prison sentences are at the center of U.S. drug policy today, yet they have been controversial almost since the outset. They are meant to ensure that sentences are uniform across the nation. Supporters argue that mandatory minimums deter criminal behavior and keep dangerous drug offenders off the streets. They leave no room for guesswork, mercy, or leniency on the part of judges, and are seen as hard evidence that the nation is serious about cracking down on drugs and crime. "Mandatory minimum sentences," says David Risley, an Illinois state prosecutor, "put steel in the spine of our criminal justice system."[20]

Yet many judges complain that mandatory sentencing laws are a "one size fits all" approach to justice. The Eighth Amendment to the Constitution protects U.S. citizens from unreasonable punishments. Mandatory minimum sentences are sometimes viewed as too extreme or out of proportion to the crime, particularly for low-level, nonviolent drug offenders. The nonprofit group Families Against Mandatory Minimums (FAMM) documents many of the cases in which low-level drug offenders are forced to spend five years or

more in state and federal prisons. In one such case, a young woman offered to give her aunt a ride to a house where the aunt was involved in the sale of seven kilos of cocaine. The woman received a ten-year sentence, plus two extra years, because her aunt was carrying a concealed weapon in the car (although the young woman testified that she knew nothing about the weapon). Frustrated with his lack of discretion in the case, the judge complained that mandatory minimum sentences "are not just absurd, but an insult to justice."[21] Federal judges often have more discretion in sentencing a murderer or rapist than a nonviolent offender convicted of possessing or selling drugs.

U.S. Customs agents arrest a suspected drug mule at a Miami airport. If convicted, he will receive a mandatory minimum prison sentence.

Overcrowded Prisons

Supporters of tough criminal sanctions for drug offenders say zero tolerance laws are working. They back this up with evidence that drug use has fallen in recent years, particularly among American high school students. But these reductions in use come at a price. In recent years, the U.S. prison population has exploded to more than 2 million people, largely due to stepped-up efforts to arrest and prosecute drug offenders. At the end of 2004, more than a quarter of all prisoners in the country were serving sentences for drug offenses, including possession, dealing drugs, or drug-related crime. In countries of Western Europe, such as England, Italy, and Germany, the rate of imprisonment is roughly 1 out of every 1,000 people in the population. In the United States it is roughly 1 out of every 143 people. Critics accuse the government of trying to arrest its way out of the illegal drug problem. The cost of housing, feeding, and caring for the current prison population is more than $40 billion per year. A former sheriff of San Francisco warns, "We desperately need the limited space in our nation's jails and prisons to house violent offenders, not minor league dope addicts and dealers."[22] High prison costs and overcrowded prisons, critics say, are signs of a failed drug policy that relies too heavily on law enforcement.

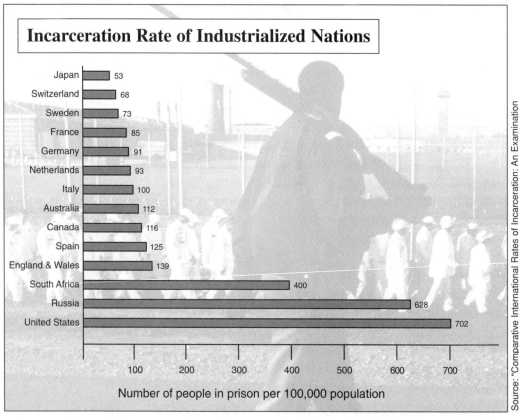

Incarceration Rate of Industrialized Nations

Country	Number of people in prison per 100,000 population
Japan	53
Switzerland	68
Sweden	73
France	85
Germany	91
Netherlands	93
Italy	100
Australia	112
Canada	116
Spain	125
England & Wales	139
South Africa	400
Russia	628
United States	702

Number of people in prison per 100,000 population

Source: "Comparative International Rates of Incarceration: An Examination of Causes and Trends." The Sentencing Project, 2003.

The Black Market Promotes Violence

Besides contributing to the problem of overcrowded prisons, tough law enforcement may also make the illegal market for drugs more violent. This is because increased pressure on dealers inflates the value of many drugs and drives up the profits for criminal groups. Under prohibition, each supplier and dealer along the drug chain adds a crime tariff. This is an amount added to the price of illegal drugs to compensate for the risks involved in dealing them, such as arrest, long prison sentences, or death at the hands of another violent, black market dealer. A sandwich bag full of powder cocaine is worth thousands of dollars, because the price is driven up as it moves along the chain from foreign suppliers, to smugglers, to dealers on the street. With such enormous amounts of money at stake, dealers have more incentive to use violence, corruption, and even murder to wipe out other dealers and seize control of drug sales.

In the United States, the black market for illegal drugs most often breeds violence in low-income, inner-city areas. These communities suffer from high rates of unemployment, poor living conditions, and heavy drug abuse. Violent drug dealers reside in these communities because there are plenty of hard-core drug customers, and police are often slow to respond to criminal activity. "The criminals continue to take another street, take another corner, take another neighborhood, and soon, they will take a whole city,"[23] cautions the pastor of a church in inner city Baltimore where drug markets are prevalent.

In foreign nations such as Colombia where cocaine and heroin are big business, the black market drug trade has given rise to a culture of extreme violence and intimidation. In Colombia, Escobar and the drug cartels of the 1980s have been replaced by violent right wing paramilitaries (unofficial militaries) and Marxist guerrillas, the opposing sides in Colombia's violent and bloody civil war. Together, these groups are estimated to earn over $1.5 billion a year from cocaine and other drugs. This allows them to purchase high-tech weapons and maintain large standing armies. In Afghanistan, more than half of the nation's economy is probably tied to drugs. Vast stretches of the remote countryside are covered in opium poppies (used to make heroin). Heroin trafficking has become the principal source of income for terrorist groups that operate in the country. Al Qaeda terrorists, for example, receive a share of profits from heroin sales in exchange for providing gunmen to protect the drug traffickers who deliver opium to Europe, America, and elsewhere in the world.

Sealing America's Borders

In fact, although a large supply of marijuana and other drugs is grown or produced domestically, most of the illegal drugs consumed in the United States are either made or have their chemical source in foreign countries. These drugs include cocaine, heroin, methamphetamine, marijuana, and Ecstasy. A critical part of America's war on drugs is law enforcement aimed at interdiction, stopping drug supply before it reaches the United States. But sealing the borders to drugs is an extremely difficult challenge.

The United States shares nearly seven thousand miles of border with Mexico and Canada, including vast stretches of wilderness, desert, and unmonitored roads and footpaths. There are another twelve thousand miles of coastline and over four hundred airports. Drugs are easily hidden in secret compartments of trucks, smuggled in with commercial goods, aboard passenger airliners and private jets, or inside the backpacks, suitcases, and clothing of individual couriers. Even when the government employs sophisticated detection equipment, traffickers are skilled at finding clever new ways to evade capture. They hide drugs in automobile parts, hollowed-out books, the secret inner lining of suitcases, and even shipments of diapers, or pay young women from South America to swallow small bags of heroin worth thousands of dollars. Searching for drugs is a little like finding a needle in a haystack, especially since a relatively small volume can supply the entire American market. It would take only thirteen large trailer trucks, for example, to supply a year's worth of cocaine.

One of the most difficult challenges for law enforcement is finding a balance between drug control efforts and the interests of law-abiding citizens. Thousands of people travel in and out of the United States every day. Billions of dollars in business transactions are conducted across the borders with Mexico and Canada. Long delays, searches, and seizures at border checkpoints cause damage to trade that is vital to the U.S. economy. Most of those who travel across the Mexican border every day, for example, do so to visit family, tour, work, or conduct business in the towns on the other side. Hundreds of trucks also pass through border checkpoints with commercial cargo. Yet Mexico is sometimes called the narcotics superhighway to the United States. Mexican drug trafficking cartels provide much of the cocaine, marijuana, heroin, and methamphetamine that

Men harvest opium poppies under the watchful eyes of armed guards in Afghanistan, whose economy is heavily dependent on heroin trafficking.

enters the country. To keep traffic flowing at the Mexican border, agents must release approximately one truck every twelve seconds. This means that they must make split-second judgments to determine which trucks or people to inspect for illegal drugs or other contraband (illegal goods.) A thorough narcotics inspection at the southern border can take up to three hours for a single forty-foot trailer. For every successful drug bust these searches produce, agents know there are many more drug smugglers who get away.

In recent years, U.S. drug control agents have made some impressive drug busts and high level arrests at the nation's borders, yet the traffickers still manage to find ways to get their products to market. Drug policy experts, such as Peter Andreas, believe it is a mistake to focus U.S. drug control efforts and resources on stopping the supply of drugs entering the country. Such efforts are largely doomed to failure, he says, because drugs are so easy to produce and

Border Patrol agents inspect a vehicle after pulling it out of a checkpoint in California. Many illegal drugs are smuggled into the United States from Mexico.

transport. "Attempts to suppress the drug supply will not succeed as long as enough of the U.S. public wants to buy drugs and profits run so high."[24]

Corruption of Public Officials

Tough U.S. prohibition policies have also contributed to the problem of widespread corruption in many of the countries where drugs are produced. Government officials, police, and law enforcement agents in these countries are eager to cash in on the huge flow of money from the U.S. drug market. They accept bribes and payoffs from dealers in return for protection, or even directly assist drug traffickers in getting their products to market. In Mexico, for example, almost every major social institution is tainted by drugs or drug money. In 1997, the Mexican ruling party was caught up in a drug corruption scandal that reached the highest levels of government, including the head of the Mexican drug control agency, members of an elite drug unit, and senior officials in the administration of former Mexican president Carlos Salinas.

Corruption and police brutality associated with the drug trade are also a widespread problem in the United States. Drug agents, police, border and prison guards, customs inspectors and others in positions of public trust, most of whom earn modest government salaries, are sometimes tempted into accepting bribes and payoffs from drug dealers. In recent years, drug-related corruption and abuse scandals have rocked local police departments in Los Angeles, New York, Cleveland, Philadelphia, Washington, D.C., New Orleans, and Savannah, Georgia. Police in these cities have been charged with stealing money from drug dealers, framing innocent people, planting false evidence, and even distributing cocaine and other drugs. Joseph McNamara, a former police chief in San Jose, California, who supports drug law reform, says that the hopelessness of preventing drug trafficking has led many officers to rationalize their own corruption. "They say, 'why should the enemy get to keep all the profits?' Guys with modest salaries are suddenly looking at $10,000 or more, and they go for it."[25]

The Drug War Is Perceived as Racist

The burden of police corruption and misconduct, like other problems related to the war on drugs, often falls disproportionately on minority and low-income communities. This has fueled the perception among residents of these communities that the war on drugs is racist. In these communities, drugs and drug abuse take a visible toll in the form of open-air drug markets, homelessness, and violence. The public nature of drug deals makes arrests far easier than in suburban neighborhoods, where drugs and money often exchange hands indoors in offices, clubs, and private homes. The rates of arrest and imprisonment in low-income, minority communities are staggering. Although African Americans make up only 12 percent of the U.S. population, they represent more than 30 percent of state and local arrests for drug offenses and more than 50 percent of those convicted (found guilty). One in every 20 black men over the age of eighteen in the United States is in state or federal prison compared to only 1 in every 180 white men—the majority for drug-related offenses.

A common drug war tactic that is viewed as racist by minority Americans is racial profiling, or the use of race or ethnicity as a factor in identifying suspected criminals. Racial profiling is frequently used in making drug-related arrests. Police officers, for example, might stop and search a car for illegal drugs based on the fact that the driver is dark-skinned. Although the officers do not have any specific evidence that the driver is engaged in criminal behavior, they believe that dark-skinned people are more likely to be involved in drug smuggling. In airports too, police often single out those they believe have the appearance of a drug courier. If a black or Caribbean passenger purchases a ticket with cash (rather than a credit card or check) or appears to be in a hurry, police grow suspicious that the money was acquired in a drug deal. In 1992, the news program *60 Minutes* aired a segment in which a well-dressed African American reporter purchased airline tickets for cash in several major airports. In each case, drug enforcement agents detained the reporter at the airport and confiscated his cash.

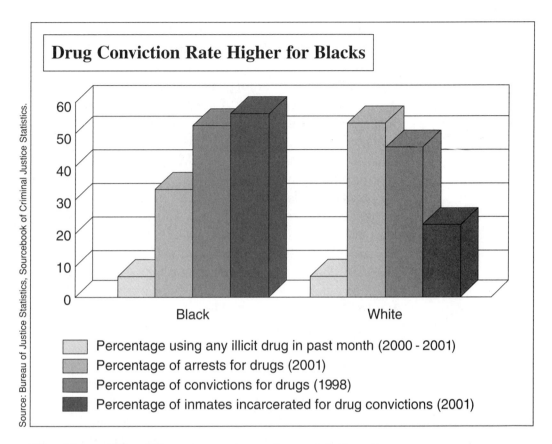

Drug Conviction Rate Higher for Blacks

Black   White

Percentage using any illicit drug in past month (2000 - 2001)
Percentage of arrests for drugs (2001)
Percentage of convictions for drugs (1998)
Percentage of inmates incarcerated for drug convictions (2001)

Source: Bureau of Justice Statistics, Sourcebook of Criminal Justice Statistics.

The Drug War Threatens Americans' Liberties

Racial profiling is not the only law enforcement tactic used in the drug war that critics say threatens Americans' individual liberties and the right to privacy. In the name of promoting zero tolerance, the U.S. government permits its drug agents to inspect Americans' bank records, record their telephone conversations, test their blood or urine, set up roadblocks to search their cars, and even inspect their trash, based on only a suspicion that they possess or are selling illegal drugs. The Fourth Amendment to the Constitution guarantees the right of Americans to be "secure in their persons, houses, papers, and effects, against unreasonable searches and seizures."[26] Yet in recent years, the courts have given the government more latitude to confiscate cash, cars, boats, homes, and other property that is acquired with the profits from illegal drugs. Government agents are permitted to seize these assets without convicting the property owner of a crime, or in some cases, without even formally filing a charge.

In the interest of curbing teen drug use, young people are also increasingly subject to intrusive procedures, such as locker searches and drug testing at school, which critics say violate their right to privacy. In his 2004 State of the Union address, President Bush proposed $23 million in new funding for schools that implement drug testing programs "as a tool to save children's lives."[27] The drug tests are usually conducted by taking a sample of a student's urine, sweat, or hair and sending it to a lab for analysis. It is an invasive and expensive procedure, yet there is little hard evidence that it helps to deter drug use among students. Recent studies point to almost identical rates of drug use at schools that test for drugs and those that do not.

Legalization proponents say the government's enthusiastic support for drug testing and other intrusive measures is one of the most dangerous consequences of the drug war. Like other decisions made by adults in a free society, they believe that drug use should be a personal decision, as long as it does not infringe on the rights of others. They say that the only sure way to restore basic liberties and reverse the violence, corruption, and racism caused by decades of zero tolerance policies is to make drugs such as marijuana and cocaine legally available for use and sale.

4

Other Approaches to the Drug Problem

IN A COFFEE SHOP in Amsterdam, the young adult customers sit at tables, sipping coffee, playing chess, reading the newspaper, and working on their laptops. The air is thick with smoke and the scent of marijuana. Many of the customers are openly smoking joints. Others are glancing at menus that list nearly a dozen varieties of marijuana, as well as baked goods laced with marijuana and hashish (also derived from the cannabis plant.) There are hundreds of such coffee shops across the Netherlands, licensed to sell small amounts of marijuana to their customers. Officially, Dutch law bans the import or possession of marijuana, but the government policy is to impose no penalties for personal use of the drug. Instead, police devote their limited time and resources to cracking down on dealers of hard drugs such as heroin, which they believe cause more long-term damage to Dutch society.

The debate over illegal drugs in the United States is often framed as an all-or-nothing choice between strict prohibition with harsh punishments for drug users and sellers, and a policy of full-scale legalization that would make heroin, cocaine, and other drugs commercially available in stores, much like alcohol or cigarettes. But in fact, there are many other approaches that have been proposed by those who seek to reform U.S. drug laws. Some, like the Dutch model, are in practice elsewhere in the world. Others have been tested on a small scale in the United States. The majority of people who

A mouth smoking a joint adorns a coffee shop window in Amsterdam, identifying the establishment as a place where marijuana can be legally bought and smoked.

devote their energies to ending the drug war, explains Ethan Nadelmann, director of the Drug Policy Alliance, a group that lobbies for drug reform, do not want to make heroin, cocaine, and all other drugs freely available over the counter. "Most drug policy reformers I know don't want crack or methamphetamine sold in 7-Elevens,"[28] he says. (In the 1990s, President Clinton's national drug czar, Barry McCaffrey, accused legalizers of wanting just that.)

Despite the tremendous resources devoted to fighting the war on drugs, and some of the toughest laws against drug use in the world, the United States consumes more illegal drugs than most other nations. Those who seek reform suggest that it is time for the country to reexamine its drug laws and consider other approaches that might be more effective.

Decriminalization

In contrast to U.S. drug prohibition and its emphasis on law enforcement and punishment, decriminalization is an approach that eliminates the criminal penalties for drug possession and personal drug use. It ensures that fewer nonviolent drug offenders tie up the criminal justice system. Under decriminalization, the production and sale of drugs remain illegal, but drug users are no longer arrested or imprisoned for possession of small quantities of drugs. Some proponents suggest that drug possession should not be considered a crime at all. Others say it should be considered a misdemeanor (a minor crime) and defendants should be charged a fine much as a driver is charged for violating a traffic law.

During the 1970s, the decriminalization approach gained increasing support in the United States. Twelve states enacted some version of marijuana decriminalization, including Oregon, Ohio, Colorado, California, Maine, and Alaska. The new laws did not make it legal to possess marijuana, since the federal prohibition remained in full force, but they did guarantee that marijuana users in these states were not subject to arrest and trial. Most of these laws remain in place today. For example, in California, a person arrested for possession of a small amount of marijuana is fined one hundred dollars. In contrast, in Michigan, where sanctions against drug use are much more severe, a person arrested with even a small amount of marijuana faces up to a year in prison and a two thousand dollar fine. In the 1970s, President Jimmy Carter spoke out in favor of decriminalizing the possession of small amounts of marijuana. He told Congress, "Penalties against possession of a drug should not be more damaging to an individual than the use of the drug itself; and where they are they should be changed." [29]

Despite Carter's endorsement, political support for decriminalization was short-lived. By the late 1970s, few of the other states were willing to consider relaxing the drug laws. In part this was due to the rising influence of a nationwide movement led by parents who were worried about the spread of marijuana among their teenage children. The crack epidemic of the 1980s and the rising crime rate in the inner cities further hardened public opinion against drug use. In the states that did decriminalize, there is little evidence to suggest that marijuana or other drug consumption went up.

Yet decriminalization has almost no impact on some of the most troubling aspects of drug prohibition. This is because it leaves drug production and sales in the hands of black market criminals. Drug policy analyst Kleiman cautions that it may not be practical to consider decriminalization on a large scale in the United States, because any increase in demand for drugs that might result from decriminalization would have dangerous consequences. Since it would still be illegal to sell these drugs, this would give violent black market suppliers and dealers even more business than they control now. "Adding more demand to a multibillion-dollar illicit industry will have disadvantages: more untaxed income, more economic activity outside legal control, and probably more corruption and violence." [30]

Harm Reduction

Like decriminalization, the harm reduction approach shifts the focus of drug control efforts away from harsh punishments for drug users. Under harm reduction, the emphasis is on the heavy drug users who represent an estimated 20 percent of all drug users in the United States, but are responsible for the greatest share of drug-related crime, disease, child abuse, theft, and other problem behaviors. Drug addicts often end up homeless and on the streets. Those who use needles to feed their habits are at high risk for spreading serious diseases such as AIDS. Supporters of harm reduction say reducing these harms is more important to the welfare of the nation than curtailing drug use or arresting drug offenders. The approach is modeled on the nation's experience in treating heavy users of alcohol and tobacco. Drug abuse, like alcoholism or cigarette smoking, is considered a public health problem, rather than a crime. Supporters argue that America will never be entirely drug-free. Instead, they are willing to tolerate a certain amount of drug use among the population in order to find practical solutions to drug-related problems.

The harm reduction approach is probably best known for needle exchange programs that allow intravenous drug users to exchange used syringes for sterile ones in order to prevent the

State Marijuana Laws

Conditional: This state has laws that allow a person to opt for probation rather than trial.

Decriminalized: No prison time or criminal record for first-time possession of a small amount for personal consumption.

Mandatory: A judge may not pass a punishment less than a Mandatory Minimum Sentence for a marijuana conviction.

Medical: Marijuana may be used in the treatment of a wide range of clinical applications.

sharing of dirty, infected needles. These programs emerged in the 1980s in response to growing alarm over the spread of HIV/AIDS. The idea behind needle exchange is that it is more important to stop the spread of AIDS than discourage drug use among those who are already addicted. In the United States, these programs must overcome stiff resistance from lawmakers. Federal laws prohibit the possession and distribution of clean syringes, and Congress bans the use of any federal money to fund needle exchange operations. This means they

A public health worker in Washington fills a paper bag with new needles and syringes to be distributed to drug users in a needle exchange program.

must either operate in defiance of the law, or find ways to get around the federal restrictions with the support of local officials. In 1999, more than 19 million sterile syringes were distributed to IV drug users in cities throughout the United States.

In Europe, where the moral arguments against drug use have less of a hold over public opinion, countries such as Switzerland, England, the Netherlands, Spain, and Italy have all experimented with harm reduction programs. Switzerland has turned to harm reduction out of desperation to manage a growing heroin problem. In 1987, the Swiss city of Zurich launched an experimental program to end years of aggressive law enforcement efforts against addicts around the city by making one local park, known as the Platzspitz, a zone of tolerance, or designated area where drug users could inject heroin, free of police interference. Police refrained from arresting intravenous users or dealers selling small quantities of heroin in the park. Officials also provided clean needles, medical care, and social services to the drug users who congregated there.

Yet the Swiss were forced to abandon the experiment two years later. "Needle Park," as it came to be known, attracted thousands of addicts from other parts of Europe. It was littered with syringes and human excrement. Crime and violence were also rampant (although the rate of crime and

AIDS did decline overall in the city). The park was eventually sealed off with steel fences, and the policy of open tolerance came to an abrupt end. Despite the failure of the Platzspitz, the Swiss did not abandon the harm reduction approach. Instead, they began experimenting with heroin maintenance clinics in many cities, where addicts can inject themselves with nonlethal doses of heroin with sterile needles under the supervision of trained, medical staff.

From a practical standpoint, critics say it would be difficult to adopt harm reduction programs on a large scale in the United States. They are often expensive and difficult to maintain. At the Swiss clinics, for example, the government must provide sterile injection equipment and a regular supply of pure heroin for users to inject three times a day. Despite the considerable expense, they can treat only a small percentage of addicts who show up on their own. In the United States, where cocaine and crack are far more prevalent than heroin, maintenance clinics and other drug management efforts would have a limited impact. Crack is not a drug that people are easily maintained on. Users receive one hit, and after the quick, intense high, they often want another. That is why no one has seriously proposed the idea of safe crack clinics for crack users, says journalist and author, Michael Massing. The major flaw with harm reduction, he says, is that it does not help addicts to quit using drugs, even when they are destroying their lives and families. It also raises the troubling question of whether it should be legal to allow people to inject or snort themselves to death. Nonetheless, Massing suggests, there is a lot to be learned from an approach that offers a more compassionate, practical alternative to punishment and jail time in controlling America's hard-core users. "Given the intense public anger that has welled up at drug addicts in recent years, any move toward tolerance is to be welcomed."[31]

Legalization

Legalization represents a more profound change in American policy than any of the other approaches to drug control. It starts with the same basic assumptions as harm reduction, that a "Drug-Free America" is an unrealistic goal. But legalization supporters believe the government should not intervene in the private lives of its citizens unless their behavior endangers the lives of other people. They point out that the reliance on law enforcement is enormously expensive and invasive, yet it has not succeeded in curbing Americans' appetite for drugs. In their view, harsh criminal sanctions against drug use threaten many of the civil liberties that lie at the foundation of American democracy, yet in the end, they only succeed in driving up enormous black market profits. Legalization is the only approach that would put an end to the violent, crime-ridden black market for illegal drugs. Instead, drug sales would be conducted in the legal marketplace where they could be more closely monitored, controlled, and even taxed.

According to supporters of legalization, a legal, open market for drugs such as marijuana and cocaine would have an immediate and dramatic impact on American society. The

A woman with a long history of heroin addiction sits in a drug center in Amsterdam, where she can shoot up the drug in relative safety.

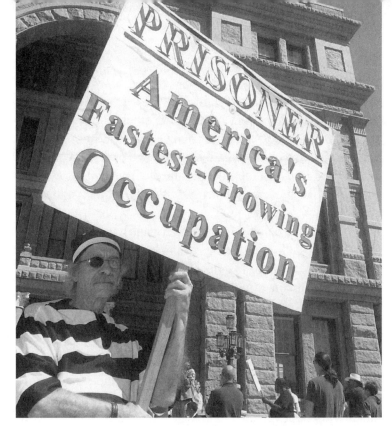

A Texas man demonstrates against drug laws that incarcerate nonviolent offenders. Proponents of legalization maintain that the criminal justice system is overburdened with drug cases.

government would greatly reduce the number of drug arrests each year and free up law enforcement around the country to focus on other priorities. Drug offenders would no longer overwhelm American prisons and court systems. Decriminalization also eases the burden on the criminal justice system, but there is an important difference. Under legalization, criminals would no longer control the drug market. Instead, drugs such as heroin and LSD would be sold legally, subject to taxation like cigarettes or alcohol. Many legalization proponents suggest the tax money could be used to support ongoing drug education and prevention efforts.

Legalization could also have significant public health benefits. The spread of HIV/AIDS among intravenous drug users could be slowed, because heroin and the clean syringes needed to inject it would be easily accessible in government clinics or stores. The government could also monitor the quality of drugs that come to market. Under the current black market system, criminal suppliers attempt to boost their profits by any means possible. They often adulterate ("cut" or mix) expensive drugs with cheaper, more toxic chemicals to keep their costs down, or increase a drug's potency in order to create more demand for it. The use of highly potent or adulterated drugs leads to many of the emergency room visits and deaths related to drug use each year. In a system in which these drugs are sold legally, they would be of known potency, unadulterated by dangerous chemicals. They might even be packaged like prescription drugs with labels that list their ingredients and potency.

Despite these benefits, most Americans have deep reservations about making dangerous drugs legally available to anyone who wants them. For decades, the nation's drug control efforts have been aimed at reducing drug use. Given the prevalence of legal drugs such as alcohol and cigarettes, there is reason to believe that the use of marijuana or cocaine might also rise if these drugs were legal. In order for legalization to work, the public must be convinced that the decline in black market violence and crime is worth the potential increase in abuse, dependence, and drug-related accidents. For those who believe drug use is immoral, any predicted increase in use is unacceptable. Former drug czar Bennett says, "Americans feel up to their hips in drugs now. They would be up to their necks under legalization."[32]

Many Americans are especially concerned about the impact that a rise in drug use would have on young people. Those under eighteen have little difficulty obtaining alcohol and engaging in heavy, sometimes reckless drinking, despite regulations that prohibit liquor sales to minors. Alcohol and tobacco companies exert great influence on American society. They market their products by making smoking and drinking seem glamorous and appealing. Critics of legalization warn that there would be little guarantee that the same thing would not occur with drugs. In the American free market system, it would be difficult to restrict newly formed drug companies from marketing their products directly to young people, since this is the segment of the population most likely to use them.

Any benefits of legalization would also be felt differently across different segments of American society. For middle- and upper-class Americans, who rarely see the crime and violence of the drug markets firsthand, these benefits may seem small. They are likely to be more concerned with the

A member of the American Medical Association holds up sweetened alcoholic beverages to show a group of teens how alcohol companies market their products to young people.

increased risk that children and other family members might become hooked on drugs. For low-income minorities, the trade-offs are less clear. Under existing laws, poor and minority Americans are disproportionately affected by the crime, violence, homelessness, and disease associated with illegal drugs. Many African American and Latino community leaders have expressed frustration with the current system. Yet they are equally worried about the effects of legalization. They fear that easy access to hard drugs such as cocaine and heroin might worsen the poverty and desperation of the inner cities by driving up the rate of drug consumption in these communities.

Supporters of legalization and other reforms face a challenging uphill battle, because in the face of so much uncertainty, most Americans are reluctant to abandon the system they know.

5

A Closer Look at Legalization

A CUSTOMER WALKS down the aisle of a drugstore and sees a small packet of heroin leaning up against the bottles of vitamins. Each packet contains a label that says, "Guaranteed Pure by the U.S. Government." A little farther down the aisle, boxes of "works" (the syringes and other gear needed to inject heroin) sit high on the shelf just out of the reach of small children. The customer brings a packet of heroin and syringe to the front counter, where he shows an ID proving that he is over twenty-one, and the clerk rings up the sale. The customer then pays in cash and leaves the store to "dope up" in the privacy of his home.

Many Americans imagine that drug legalization would look something like this. Understandably, the idea of making addictive drugs like heroin and cocaine readily available for sale at the local drugstore or supermarket makes them uneasy. Yet a system in which users purchase drugs in stores just as they would buy office supplies or soda is not what most legalization proponents have in mind.

The roughly 15 percent of Americans who support the idea of drug legalization agree that it is time to put an end to what they see as years of misguided drug policies. Yet they have very different views about what legalization would look like in practice. Some envision government-operated stores where drugs would be sold according to strict rules, and sales to minors would be prohibited. Others suggest that drugs would be available in privately run clinics, clubs, or coffee shops licensed by the government.

All of the different approaches to legalization would involve a total reversal of current laws and policies, but they have never been tested on a large scale in the United States or elsewhere. This is what makes most Americans so reluctant to accept or even consider them. If legalization is to rise above the level of "idle chitchat"[33] says Representative

Many proponents of legalization envision establishments like this one in the Netherlands where drugs may be legally and safely purchased.

Charles Rangel, who represents a mainly low-income African American district in New York City where drugs have taken a heavy toll, legalizers must first answer a long list of tough-minded, practical questions. Among the questions Rangel poses, which drugs should be permitted? How would they be sold? Would users be permitted to buy as much of a drug as they wanted? Or would there be a customer limit? If so, how would it be enforced? Until answers to these questions are forthcoming, he says, drug legalization will not be taken seriously either by U.S. lawmakers or the American public.

In recent years, legalization supporters have begun to provide answers to these practical questions and others. While some of the details have yet to be filled in, they are laying out their plans for a society in which drugs such as cocaine and marijuana are made legally available for use and sale.

The Alcohol and Tobacco Model

There is one practical, real-world model for drug legalization in the United States, and that is the way that alcohol and tobacco are produced and sold. These two legal drugs are widely available throughout the country in liquor stores, supermarkets, bars, and restaurants. They are manufactured and sold by private companies that compete aggressively for business, but they are also subject to special regulations and taxes. For instance, cigarettes may not be advertised on television, sold to minors, or smoked in most public buildings. Since 1965 each packet of cigarettes has also carried a warning from the U.S. Surgeon General about the dangers of smoking. In the case of alcohol, liquor may be sold only in restaurants, stores, and bars that receive a license from the state, and sales are prohibited to anyone under the age of twenty-one. Yet even with these restrictions, alcohol and cigarette companies continue to make huge profits. They sponsor high-profile sporting and cultural events and use their corporate power and money to help fund political campaigns and influence government decision making.

Yet it is widely recognized that the products these companies market cause tremendous social harm. The health care costs for alcohol and cigarettes are higher than those for all other illegal drugs combined. Excessive consumption of alcohol results in a third of all deaths and injuries from car accidents. It is linked to most of the rapes (as many as 90 percent) that occur on college campuses. Its use during pregnancy causes fetal alcohol syndrome, which is linked to a range of developmental disorders in children. More prisoners currently serving time in state prisons across the country were drunk on alcohol than high on drugs when they committed their crimes. Tobacco also inflicts heavy suffering and damage. This year alone, more than four hundred thousand people will die because they smoked, and many more will suffer from cancer, lung disease, and other ailments. "The harm caused by alcohol and cigarettes, is, if anything, a reason not to treat illegal drugs in the same manner,"[34] say William Bennett, John DiIulio, and John Walters, the coauthors of *Body Count,* a book on winning the war on crime and drugs.

Legalization supporters say this attitude is hypocritical. There is nothing in the legal definition of a drug that exempts alcohol or tobacco. Both are potentially addictive substances. Despite the social harms caused by these legal drugs, most people believe that the choice to smoke or drink, especially in private, should remain a personal decision. Few would ever consider throwing someone in jail for being an alcoholic or a chain smoker. In contrast with marijuana and other drugs, alcohol and cigarettes simply have a long history of social acceptance in America. A ban on alcohol and tobacco, the two most widely used drugs in the nation among people of all ages, would be extremely difficult, if not impossible to enforce.

Setting a Price for Drugs

Under legalization, the ban on drugs such as marijuana and cocaine would also be lifted and they would be bought and sold in the legal marketplace like alcohol and tobacco. The main advantage of this would be to wipe out the huge prof-

Source: United States Department of Health and Human Services, Centers for Disease Control and Prevention.

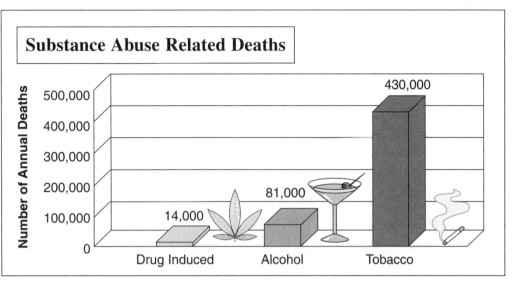

its, violence, and disorder that accompany the black market for illegal drugs. Supporters of legalization point to the experience of alcohol prohibition early in the twentieth century. When the Eighteenth Amendment to the Constitution prohibiting alcohol sales and manufacture was lifted in 1933 (personal possession and use of alcohol were never prohibited), black market suppliers and organized criminals were forced out of the liquor business. Legal manufacturers stepped in to produce and sell enough liquor to satisfy Americans' demand.

In the case of illegal drugs, the key to driving criminal suppliers out of business would be in pricing drugs low enough to undersell the black market, but high enough to discourage more people from using them. If prices dropped too low, more people might be encouraged to try drugs. In addition to the dangers increased drug use would bring, legal suppliers might not be able to meet the rising consumer demand, and this could spur black market criminals to enter the business again. Another difficulty in meeting consumer demand would be in providing enough of a variety of drugs—from PCP to Ecstasy to meth—to satisfy the tastes of U.S. drug users. Some also fear that private drug companies might have an incentive to market and create demand for new drugs. To make sure this would not happen, some propose passing laws that would prevent suppliers from introducing a drug such as methamphetamine into a market in which it was not already in use among the local population.

How Would Drugs Be Sold?

One way to ensure that drugs are priced high enough to discourage use and low enough to drive out black market dealers is to establish state-sponsored retail drug outlets. At these outlets, the prices, distribution, and quality of drugs could be tightly controlled. Thirteen states, including Pennsylvania, Utah, and Virginia, already control the retail sale of alcohol in this way. Legalizers who support this plan say the profits that states collect from the retail outlets could be used to combat drug abuse and fund prevention and treatment efforts.

Another approach is to leave drug sales to private companies, since they would be more likely to produce drugs efficiently and offer a lower price. The government could discourage increased use by adding a tax to the price of the drugs, like the tax that is added to a pack of cigarettes. These drug taxes would provide a huge new source of money for federal and state governments that could also be used for ongoing education and prevention efforts. But finding just the right rate of taxation would be difficult. If drug taxes were set too high, black market suppliers could continue to provide the drugs at a lower price. This would also mean that heavy users, many of whom do not have regular, full-time jobs, would still be forced to find money to support their habits by stealing or dealing drugs themselves.

Still another approach to selling drugs is modeled on the idea of the Dutch marijuana coffee shops. Drug use would be restricted to a limited number of privately owned coffee shops or clubs, which would be licensed by the government to sell drugs in small quantities to their adult customers. As in the Netherlands, the shops would not be allowed to advertise or market their products; the government would maintain the right to shut down those that became troublesome or violated the law. A potential problem with this approach is how to handle an increase in "drug tourism." The marijuana coffee shops in the Netherlands draw visitors from all over Europe. Similarly, in the United States, it would be difficult to keep people from traveling to the clubs from out of town, prevent rowdy or aggressive behavior in the neighborhoods surrounding them, and ensure that people did not drive home under the influence of drugs.

Marijuana is measured into a container at a Dutch pharmacy. Some proponents of legalization look to the Dutch model of government-licensed sale of soft drugs.

Demand for Drugs under Legalization

What most Americans fear about all of these approaches to legalization is that they would drive up demand for drugs and create a huge population of drug addicts and abusers. Yet there is no way to predict with any certainty how many people would try drugs if they became legal. This is because it is difficult to know how many people are deterred from using drugs by current laws prohibiting drug use, the threat of arrest, or the search time that it takes to track down illegal sources of drug supply. Under existing law, many Americans would not even know where to go to find hard drugs like crack cocaine or heroin. It is much easier to resist drug use when the purchase involves a drive into an unfamiliar, or crime-ridden part of the city, instead of a quick trip to the local drug outlet.

Police in Washington, D.C., arrest a man suspected of dealing PCP. Some critics contend that legalization of soft drugs would lead more users to experiment with hard drugs like PCP.

With drugs readily available and the legal barriers to using them removed, it is highly likely that more Americans would experiment with drugs. Some of those who tried drugs for the first time would eventually become heavy users and addicts. Critics of legalization warn that the rate of addiction and overdose would soar to levels never seen before. The nation would face greater health care costs, highway accidents, and hospital emergency room visits. The availability of inexpensive, legal drugs might also heighten the problems of poverty-stricken inner city areas. More people could turn to drugs, as they do to cheap alcohol, for an easy escape from the hardships of poverty.

Supporters of legalization say these fears are greatly exaggerated. Polls show that most people would not change their habits or start to use new drugs, even if they were legally available. To support their case, legalizers often cite the example of the Netherlands, where it has been more than thirty years since the government relaxed its policy on the possession and personal use of marijuana. Although marijuana use in the Netherlands rose in the 1980s and early 1990s, at a time when the number of coffee shops serving cannabis increased in many Dutch cities, there has been no evidence of an increase in hard drug use or drug-related crime.

Drug Crime under Legalization

One of the most powerful arguments for legalizing drugs is that it would eliminate an enormous black market that breeds violence, corruption, and crime. Legalization supporters accept a possible rise in drug use as the price the nation must pay in order to reduce crime. The alternative, they say, is to allow the high level of violent crime linked to the illegal market in an attempt to hold down rates of drug use and addiction. In reality, the relationship between drugs and crime is more complicated. Legalization would not stop all crime associated with drugs. Alcohol is legal, yet many people under the influence of alcohol abuse their children and families, drive under the influence, rape, rob, and murder. Similarly, heavy use of some drugs, including stimulants such as cocaine, methamphetamine, and PCP, and muscle-enhancing anabolic steroids are known to cause aggressive, violent behavior.

Yet much of the violent crime related to drugs is tied to the black market. Violent, ruthless criminals are attracted to the illegal drug trade because they are willing to take great risks in exchange for the enormous potential profits to be gained. These violent criminals often settle their disputes violently. Conservative social critic and legalization supporter David Boaz points out, "You don't see shootouts in the car, liquor, or tobacco business. But if you have a dispute with another [drug] dealer, if he rips you off, you can't sue him, you can't take him to court, you can't do anything except use violence." [35]

In a system in which drugs were legal and affordable, crimes such as theft, prostitution, and vandalism could also decline. Heavy drug users often commit these crimes in order to obtain money or goods to pay high black market prices for drugs such as heroin and cocaine. Desperate addicts will often go to any lengths to get the drugs they need, selling their bodies for sex, stealing the money from friends or family, or hocking anything that is valuable enough to sell. Many of these heavy users also become repeat offenders. They end up in and out of the criminal justice system, tying up the courts and prisons and costing taxpayers large sums of money to keep them off the streets.

Advertising

Critics of legalization warn that any reductions in black market crime would come at too high a price. They imagine a society in which the social norms against drug use would disappear and drug companies would be free to advertise dangerous products like heroin. Residents of any major city could drive down the highway and look up at a billboard printed with the slogan, "This cocaine's for you," or turn on their car radios and hear a jingle with the lyrics, "Get stoned on pot this weekend." In reality, most legalization proponents do not support the idea of unrestricted advertising for drug companies selling their products. Instead, they

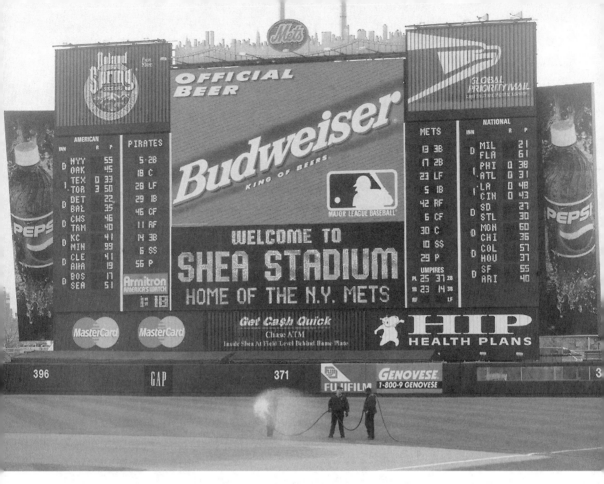

suggest that advertising should be prohibited or limited to specific media outlets, such as magazines with an adult circulation. They cite the example of the Netherlands, where the nation's marijuana coffee shops have been banned from advertising since they were first established more than thirty years ago. Visitors must find these shops by looking for a special flag on the door, purchasing an unofficial map, or asking a local resident to direct them.

In the United States, restrictions on advertising would be difficult. "The U.S. experience regulating other dangerous vices is not encouraging," say drug policy analysts Reuter and MacCoun. "State and federal governments have ended up allowing gambling, smoking, and drinking to be heavily promoted in the marketplace, despite the overwhelming evidence that they cause great harm to many people"[36] One clear sign that alcohol and tobacco companies have been successful in marketing their products is the fact that Americans spend approximately $490 billion a year on alcoholic beverages, more than twice as much as they spend on all illegal drugs combined. Reuter and MacCoun warn that drug sales might also climb dramatically if private companies began to market drugs as aggressively as they do alcohol and tobacco. To prevent this from happening, legalization supporters say the U.S. government could continue to promote antidrug messages on popular media and entertainment outlets. In the past, the ONDCP has sponsored ads with Internet search companies that automatically pop up on the computer screens of people who search for terms such as "pot," "coke," or "weed." "As long as these kinds of efforts are made," says legalization proponent Husak, "no one should be tempted to think the state condones or approves of illicit drug use."[37]

Legalization and America's Youth

Among proponents of legalization, there is nearly universal agreement that access to drugs should be banned for anyone under the age of twenty-one. Most suggest putting laws in

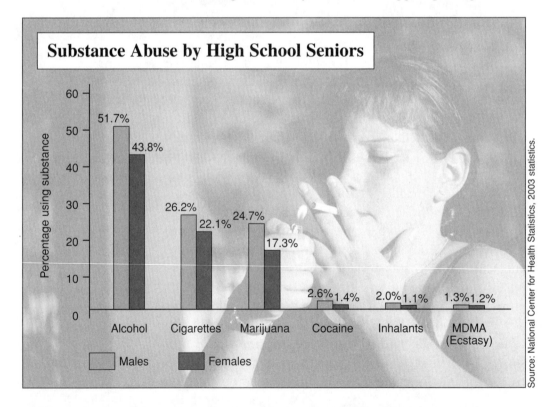

Substance Abuse by High School Seniors

Percentage using substance

Alcohol: Males 51.7%, Females 43.8%
Cigarettes: Males 26.2%, Females 22.1%
Marijuana: Males 24.7%, Females 17.3%
Cocaine: Males 2.6%, Females 1.4%
Inhalants: Males 2.0%, Females 1.1%
MDMA (Ecstasy): Males 1.3%, Females 1.2%

Males   Females

Source: National Center for Health Statistics, 2003 statistics.

place that would require buyers to show proof of age with a driver's license or other ID when making a drug purchase, and punishing retailers who sell to minors by confiscating their business licenses and shutting them down. Legalization is meant to be a system in which drugs are legally available to adults, not to children.

Protecting children in the midst of widespread legal adult use of drugs would not be easy, but legalization proponents say that children are not protected now. Despite the strong antidrug messages they receive in school prevention programs and on TV and other media, teens continue to experiment with drugs. Most teens say they face little difficulty gaining access to illegal drugs such as marijuana. Yet it is the two legal drugs, alcohol and tobacco, that are most frequently used and abused by American young people. Critics fear that under legalization, drugs such as marijuana and cocaine would replace alcohol as the new symbols of adult status among teens.

Whenever laws treat young people differently than adults, or allow adults to do something that children are not permitted to do, some of what is available to adults "trickles down" to the nation's youth. This is true not only of alcohol and cigarettes, but also of other restricted consumer items, such as pornographic magazines and even handguns. Legalization supporters argue that the solution should not be prohibition for everyone. Husak uses the example of violent or sexual images on television or the Internet. If the nation really was serious about "minimizing the likelihood that children will be exposed to violence or sex," he says, "we would ban these pictures for everyone, across the board. That option, however, is intolerable."[38] Instead, parents scramble cable signals, disable computers, and maintain viewing rules within their own homes and families.

America has learned to live with tobacco, gambling, alcohol, and pornography. Legalization supporters argue that the nation should adopt a similar policy when it comes to drugs. Especially in the case of less addictive drugs, such as marijuana, they say it does not make sense for the U.S. government to punish and restrict adults in order to prevent children from using them.

6

Legalizing
Marijuana

IN AUGUST 1996, more than a hundred armed law enforcement agents stormed the San Francisco Cannabis Buyers' Club. They broke down the door and seized 150 pounds of marijuana that the club planned to distribute to its members, some of whom suffered from serious diseases such as AIDS, cancer, and glaucoma. The club's founders had been allowed to operate illegally for years while San Francisco police looked the other way. But the U.S. government alleged that they were running a marijuana distribution ring. A federal narcotics agent, posing undercover as a patient, had joined the club without showing valid medical papers and purchased marijuana in amounts that exceeded what was needed for medical use. The government also claimed to have videotape evidence that the club was selling marijuana to teenagers and allowing young children to remain in the building while their parents smoked upstairs. The Cannabis Buyers' Club was forced to shut down, and hundreds of ill patients in the San Francisco area lost their access to legal marijuana.

Less than three months after the raid, voters in California and Arizona passed state ballot initiatives approving the use of medical marijuana to treat seriously ill patients. By 2004, ten states and the District of Columbia had passed similar ballot initiatives. A *Time*/CNN poll in 2002 found that while only 34 percent of Americans would consider legalizing marijuana completely, close to 80 percent think it is acceptable to dispense marijuana for medical purposes. A large majority of Americans also say that people caught with marijuana for recreational use should receive a fine rather than a prison sentence. Although most politicians and members of the public remain firmly opposed to full-scale drug legalization, popular momentum is growing for changes in the way the nation treats marijuana.

How Dangerous Is Marijuana?

The U.S. government classifies marijuana as a highly dangerous, Schedule I drug and prohibits its use, except in rare circumstances. Yet most scientists say marijuana does not

A disabled man selects marijuana muffins at a Cannabis Buyers Cooperative in California. Many Americans approve of the use of marijuana for medical reasons.

merit its placement with drugs that have the "highest potential for abuse." Unlike other Schedule I drugs such as heroin, marijuana does not typically cause physical dependence or withdrawal symptoms. (Some studies do suggest that long-term, heavy marijuana users may experience physical dependence.) Research on marijuana is limited, however, because the U.S. government restricts access to the drug, even for study. As a result, scientists are only just beginning to understand the ways in which THC, the potent psychoactive or mind-altering ingredient in marijuana, acts in the brain. Most agree that marijuana is less physically addictive than legal drugs such as alcohol and tobacco.

In its early drug prevention messages of the 1930s and 1940s, the U.S. government often exaggerated the dangers of marijuana smoking. The term reefer madness was first used as the title of a 1936 film and came to refer to the crazed behavior supposedly induced by smoking reefer or dope (slang for marijuana) that would incite users to violence or cause them to act out in extreme paranoia. The idea of "reefer madness" was ridiculed in the 1960s and 1970s as more young people began to smoke marijuana and found that their own experiences did not match the government's exaggerated, often hysterical depictions of the drug.

Groups that oppose marijuana reforms have focused on the idea that marijuana is a gateway drug that can lead to the use of harder, more addictive substances. Many hard drug users first smoke marijuana before moving on to drugs such as cocaine, heroin, or methamphetamine. (They also often drink alcohol.) Scientists, however, dispute the idea that there is anything about the chemistry of marijuana that produces a physical craving for more addictive drugs. It is more likely that because marijuana is the most widely used and available illegal drug in the United States, it is also the first illegal drug most people encounter. Marijuana sometimes leads to hard drug use because many of the risk factors that make people willing to try marijuana also make them willing to try other illegal drugs. Teens who smoke marijuana, for example, often find themselves at parties or other social situations in which illegal drugs

are present. They may be pressured by peers or, in some cases, dealers looking to make more money on expensive drugs, to try something a little more "daring."

Pro-marijuana activists, on the other hand, typically downplay any potential risks of using marijuana. In Web sites, chat rooms, and marijuana-themed magazines that attract a devoted readership, they promote free and open access to marijuana for adults over the age of twenty-one, and they praise the drug's natural healing properties and power to produce an intense sensory experience. They also point out that no one dies from smoking marijuana as can happen with heroin or cigarettes. One statistic that is often heard in pro-marijuana circles is that it would take a 160-pound person nine hundred joints in a sitting to reach a lethal dose.

Marijuana, however, can pose serious behavioral and health risks to users in some circumstances. Marijuana is known to alter users' depth perception and sense of time. It slows physical reactions and impairs motor skills. It is most dangerous in situations in which people must react quickly, such as driving a car or operating heavy machinery. Marijuana also interferes with the ability to complete

Young men roll joints at a New York City march in support of marijuana legalization. Younger people tend to downplay the drug's risks.

tasks that require coordination and concentration, such as sports, acting, or studying. When used to excess by the 2 to 3 million Americans who smoke several joints a day, marijuana can seriously disrupt schoolwork, jobs, or home life.

Repeated use of marijuana can also cause long-term health problems. Frequent smoking can damage the lungs and immune system, and may be a risk factor in respiratory cancer. Pregnant or nursing women who ingest marijuana increase the risk of having low-birth weight babies. For people who are prone to mental illness, marijuana may present the greatest potential danger. Many people who suffer from untreated depression or schizophrenia, for example, tend to self-medicate in order to feel better. In these cases, marijuana can worsen the symptoms of their mental illness. A 1999 survey by the government's Substance Abuse and Mental Health Services Administration revealed that teens associate regular marijuana use with behaviors such as social withdrawal, anxiety, depression, and attention problems. Those who were weekly marijuana users were three times more likely than nonusers to have thoughts of committing suicide. What is not clear is whether marijuana causes these problems, or, more likely, if teens who become heavy users have troubled lives before they turn to the drug.

The Politics of Marijuana

In political terms, marijuana is the most important and controversial illegal drug in America. If marijuana were made legally available, the country's drug problem would shrink dramatically. Instead of 19 million current illegal drug users, there would be closer to 4 million. These users would still represent a serious problem, but their smaller total numbers would make it much harder to justify the same level of commitment to the war on drugs. There are approximately seven hundred thousand arrests for marijuana offenses in the United States each year, nearly half of these for possession only. Estimates of current spending on marijuana enforcement are between $5 billion and $7 billion per year. While this is less than the amount spent on hard drugs such as cocaine, if marijuana were made legally available, it would represent significant savings for federal and state governments.

Marijuana receives a large share of law enforcement energy and resources, even though the black market for the drug is far less violent and disruptive to American society than the market for other more dangerous substances. Marijuana is rarely purchased in inner-city street markets where the illegal drug trade in the United States has such a devastating impact on families and neighborhoods. The price per dose is not nearly as inflated as the price of addictive drugs such as cocaine or heroin, so it is not a major factor in enriching murderous foreign drug lords or corrupting public officials. "Marijuana dealers are not shooting up the cities," says drug policy analyst Kleiman. " . . . Marijuana addicts are not stealing to pay for their drug habits, marijuana use and associated sexual activity are not spreading syphilis and AIDS, victims of marijuana are not clamoring for admission to treatment or flocking into self-help groups."[39]

Nevertheless, marijuana has become a powerful symbol in the struggle over America's cultural and moral values. Pro-marijuana activists portray marijuana smoking not simply as a way to relax or get high, but as an expression of personal freedom in the face of increasing government and corporate control over people's private lives. In an essay criticizing the criminal prohibition of marijuana, Ira Glasser, former executive director of the civil rights group, the American Civil Liberties Union, writes that "marijuana users are not the only victims of such a policy [of criminalizing marijuana use] because a government that crosses easily over into this zone of personal behavior will cross over into others."[40]

Opponents of marijuana reform, on the other hand, perceive the drug as a corrupting influence on young people and a threat to religious and family values. They often associate the drug with the permissive social climate of the 1960s and 1970s and fear that any attempt to change marijuana's status would signal a return to the youth-centered,

Demonstrators carry signs in support of marijuana, the most widely used illegal drug in the United States. It is unlikely that marijuana will be legalized any time soon.

countercultural attitudes of that era. Marijuana conjures up for them images of hippies in tie-dye, dropping out, getting stoned, and protesting the Vietnam War, or burning the American flag. Their staunch opposition to the drug extends to the use of marijuana for medical use. They believe that allowing even limited use of marijuana is a slippery slope that will began an irreversible slide toward full-scale legalization.

Legalizing Marijuana

Yet most supporters of marijuana legalization do not suggest that marijuana be made available like other consumer items. Instead, they propose a system in which marijuana sales would be subject to special taxes and regulations aimed at encouraging users to exercise self-control and smoke the drug only under controlled circumstances. Strict regulations would ensure that marijuana use would still be treated as a serious criminal offense in situations in which it could endanger people's lives, including driving, operating heavy machinery, flying airplanes, and performing surgery.

One popular model for marijuana legalization is the Dutch cannabis coffee shops that are permitted to sell small amounts of marijuana or hashish to their adult customers. Other approaches involve tighter control over marijuana's use and sale. Drug policy analyst Kleiman proposes a system in which people who choose to purchase marijuana would have to apply for a personal license with a quantity limit assigned to them. They would be able to obtain their supply of marijuana from retail stores that resemble the government liquor outlets that operate in some states today, or alternately, by mail order. These government outlets would have access to a registry of users that they could call to verify a customer's status much like store clerks call to validate a credit card purchase. Any potential purchaser convicted of a crime connected to his or her drug use, such as driving under the influence or distributing marijuana to minors, would face permanent loss of the license.

Supporters say these and other approaches to legalization would be more effective in controlling marijuana use than current prohibition policies. Yet legalization leaves too much uncertainty about rising drug rates, crime, accidents, and undesirable, drug-induced behavior to persuade most Americans, or elected officials, to overturn current laws and policies. A total repeal of marijuana laws is probably not in the nation's immediate political future. Instead, proponents of drug reform have begun to focus their efforts on smaller, more incremental changes in the nation's marijuana policies that have a greater chance of being realized.

Medical Marijuana

In recent years, the debate over legalization has shifted to medical marijuana and its benefits in treating seriously ill patients. Medical marijuana activists promote the drug as an effective treatment in controlling the pain, nausea, muscle spasms, and appetite loss caused by a wide range of ailments, including epilepsy, multiple sclerosis (MS), glaucoma, cancer, and AIDS. "It's tragic," says physician and marijuana activist Lester Grinspoon, "that marijuana—a drug as versatile and inexpensive and nontoxic as the wonder drug of the forties, penicillin—isn't medically available."[41]

Most doctors react more cautiously to using medical marijuana. Some are uncomfortable with the idea of a medicine that must be smoked to be effective, saying that this can cause damage to the lungs and respiratory system. They fear that legitimizing smoking for medical reasons would undermine the successful antismoking campaign that has stopped thousands of teens from using cigarettes. Others object to the idea that a medicine should have psychoactive properties that cause users to experience a "high." A growing number of medical professionals, however, believe that while marijuana is not a miracle drug or cure-all, it may be useful in treating diseases for which there are few other alternatives. A 1991 Harvard University survey of oncologists (cancer specialists) revealed that of the roughly one-third of oncologists nationwide who responded to the survey, half would recommend marijuana to their cancer patients as a way to reduce the nausea associated with chemotherapy (the powerful drug treatment used to stop the spread of cancer). In some cases, they had already counseled patients to use marijuana even though there was no legal way for them to obtain the drug.

In recent years, many Americans have come to believe that decisions to use marijuana for health reasons should be entrusted to doctors and patients, and not to politicians. In every state in which the issue has reached the ballot, voters have expressed approval, often by large margins, for medical marijuana reforms. By 2005, twelve states—California, Arizona, Alaska, Oregon, Colorado, Nevada, Washington, Hawaii, Maryland, Vermont, Maine, and Montana—had adopted medical marijuana laws, most of them by putting the issue to a popular vote.

The specifics of how these laws are to be carried out vary by state. In some states, a doctor's note or prescription is sufficient to qualify someone for a supply of marijuana. In others, patients are required to carry a medical ID card or enter their names in an official registry. In California, the variety of outlets that have emerged since marijuana was legalized for medical use range from pharmacy-like stores to medical coffee shops and buyers' clubs. (The federal government has continued to try to shut down some of the

An elderly woman in California protests the arrest of personnel at government-licensed medical marijuana dispensaries. Many doctors believe marijuana to be beneficial to the terminally ill.

cannabis clubs and other outlets.) Although these outlets are authorized to serve only people who carry a patient ID card or a signed recommendation from a licensed doctor, critics suggest that the requirements are not restrictive enough to protect against abuse. Some patients who suffer from serious diseases such as cancer and AIDS become lifetime members of the cannabis buyers' clubs, for example, but the clubs also "treat" people with minor complaints who manage to obtain a doctor's consent. In 1997, reporter Hanna Rosin criticized the medical marijuana movement for not being honest about its primary aim of legalizing marijuana. She described a scene at the San Francisco Cannabis Buyers' Club in which not only the terminally ill, but stragglers, homeless people, aging hippies, and others stood in line at the door, waiting to get high and relieve minor ailments such as insomnia or migraine headaches.

The Impact of Legalizing Marijuana on America's Youth

The greatest fear of those who oppose legalizing marijuana under any circumstances, including medical use, is that making the drug legitimate will encourage more young people to use it. One of the ways in which the federal government has responded to growing popular support for medical marijuana reforms is to step up its efforts to curb teen use of the drug. As part of this effort, the ONDCP launched a new series of public service ads during Super Bowl 2003. In one of the ads, a mother and father stare at their teenage daughter after they have just discovered that she is pregnant. In disbelief the mother holds up a plastic applicator from the pregnancy test. "Poor judgment is one way your life can be changed by marijuana," the television voice-over says. "It's more harmful than we thought."[42] Although the ads' sponsors say the aggressive media and prevention campaign has succeeded in changing attitudes toward marijuana among American teens, more than half of all U.S. students continue to try marijuana before graduating from high school. More than 80 percent of seniors say the drug is easy or fairly easy to obtain.

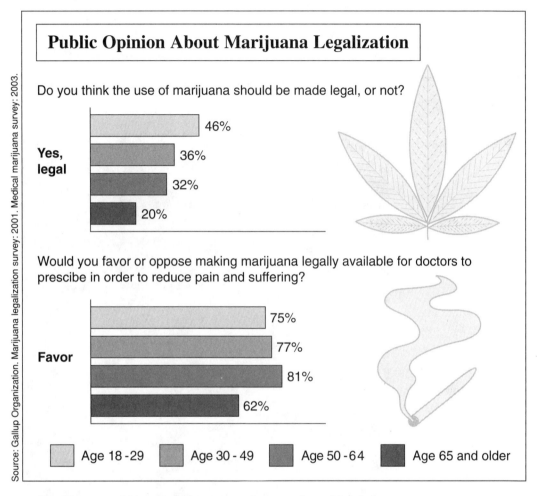

Source: Gallup Organization. Marijuana legalization survey: 2001. Medical marijuana survey: 2003.

Public Opinion About Marijuana Legalization

Do you think the use of marijuana should be made legal, or not?

Yes, legal
46%
36%
32%
20%

Would you favor or oppose making marijuana legally available for doctors to prescibe in order to reduce pain and suffering?

Favor
75%
77%
81%
62%

Age 18 -29　　Age 30 - 49　　Age 50 -64　　Age 65 and older

Yet if aggressive prevention campaigns and punitive laws and policies have not prevented young people from using marijuana, it is not clear what would happen if the drug became legally available for sale to adults over the age of twenty-one. The example of alcohol suggests that use among teens would probably rise. Some marijuana would be diverted from legal outlets for teen use. Teens would also obtain the drug from adults or use false IDs and other criminal means to get a hold of it. Most approaches to marijuana legalization leave prohibition in effect for young people, but seldom consider how underage users should be treated if they are caught using the drug. Many youth advocacy groups say it would be a mistake to maintain harsh laws and punishments for young people, even as the drug is made legally available to adults. If the nation truly wants to protect young people, they say, it must turn away from punitive policies and stop seeing young drug users as a danger to society. Instead, groups such as Students for Sensible Drug Policies (SSDP), which is run by students on the nation's

Demonstrators in Texas demand softer drug laws. Today, many people believe that incarceration does little to stop drug use and that current drug policies are in dire need of reform.

college campuses, propose a more "compassionate" and "sensible" approach to reducing teen drug use. This includes open and honest education, discussion that helps young people to ask questions, and counseling in which they are treated with respect and those who use marijuana and other drugs are not punished, but encouraged to reduce their use and seek help when they need it.

This emphasis on more compassionate, practical alternatives to current drug policies is shared by many of those who support drug law reform. Although the get-tough approach to illegal drugs continues to dominate the political debate in America, more people have come to believe that law enforcement and punishment alone cannot resolve problems such as drug-related crime and addiction. Only a small minority is willing to consider full-scale drug legalization, but residents of cities and states across the nation are supporting reforms such as a change in the status of medical marijuana, less severe punishments for nonviolent drug offenders, and treatment and support to help hardcore addicts turn their lives around.

Notes

Introduction

1. Quoted in Allison North Jones, "The Media Business: Advertising; Strong Views, Pro and Con, on Ads Linking Drug Use to Terrorism," *New York Times,* April 2, 2002, p. C7.

Chapter 1: Illegal Drug Use in America

2. Quoted in Craig Horowitz, "Drugs Are Bad: The Drug War Is Worse," *New York Magazine,* February 5, 1996, p. 30.

3. L.D. Johnston, P.M. O'Malley, J.G. Bachman, & J.E. Schulenberg, *Monitoring the Future National Survey Results on Drug Use, 1975–2003: vol. I: Secondary School Students.* Bethesda, MD: National Institute on Drug Abuse, 2003, p. 35. www.monitoringthefuture.org.

4. Johnston, O'Malley, Bachman, and Schulenberg, *Monitoring the Future National Survey Results on Drug Use,* p. 36.

5. Johnston, O'Malley, Bachman, and Schulenberg, *Monitoring the Future National Survey Results on Drug Use,* p. 13.

Chapter 2: Why Are Drugs Illegal?

6. Quoted in *New York Times,* "No Change in Basics: Bush Rejects Any Fundamental Shift, Instead Vowing Unprecedented Vigor," September 6, 1989, p. A11.

7. Quoted in Christopher Wren, "The Opposing Camps Square Off at a Congressional Hearing About Drug Legalization," *New York Times,* June 20, 1999, Section 1, p. 28.

8. Quoted in Dan Baum, *Smoke and Mirrors: The War on Drugs and the Politics of Failure,* Boston: Little Brown, 1996, p. 72.

9. Quoted in Harry G. Levine and Craig Reinarman, "The Politics of America's Latest Drug Scare," in Richard O. Curry, ed., *Freedom at Risk: Secrecy, Censorship, and Repression in the 1980s.* Philadelphia: Temple University Press, 1988, Chapter 17. www.psychedelic-library.org/drug_politics.htm.

10. Craig Reinarman and Harry G. Levine, "The Construction of America's Crack Crisis," 1995. www.drugtext.org/library/articles/craig2.html.

11. Quoted in George J. Church, "Thinking the Unthinkable: As Frustration Mounts over a Failed Policy, Serious People Are Asking: Why Not End the Crime and Profits by Making Drugs Legal?" *Time,* May 30, 1988.

12. Douglas Husak, *Legalize This! the case for decriminalizing drugs.* London: Verso, 2002, p. 68.

13. William J. Bennett, John J. DiIulio Jr., and John P. Walters, *Body Count: Moral Poverty . . . and How to Win America's War Against Crime and Drugs.* New York: Simon & Schuster, 1996, p. 27.

14. Bruce D. Glasscock, "Testimony Before Congress: Glasscock Testimony on Decriminalization of Illegal Drugs," International Association of Police Chiefs, July 13, 1999. www.theiacp.org/documents/index.cfm?document_id=60&fuseaction=document&subtype_id=1.

15. Mark A.R. Kleiman, *Against Excess: Drug Policy for Results.* New York: BasicBooks, 1992, p. 292.

16. Quoted in Bennett, Di Iulio Jr., and Walters, *Body Count,* p. 141.

17. Quoted in Church, "Thinking the Unthinkable."

Chapter 3: The War on Drugs and Its Costs

18. Kleiman, *Against Excess,* p. 4.

19. Husak, *Legalize This!,* p. 153.

20. David Risley, "Mandatory Minimum Sentences: An Overview," Drug Watch International, May 2000. www.drugwatch.org/Mandatory%20Minimum%20Sentences.htm.

21. Quoted in Families Against Mandatory Minimums, "Mandatory Sentencing Was Once America's Law-and-Order Panacea: Here's Why It's Not Working: Primer on Mandatory Minimums." www.famm.org/ac_beginners_guide.htm.

22. Quoted in Peter Andreas, "U.S. Drug Control Policy," November 1996. www.fpif.org/briefs/vol1/drugs_body.html.

23. Quoted in Gary Gately, "Baltimore Struggles to Battle Witness Intimidation," *Boston Globe,* February 12, 2005, p. A3.

24. Peter Andreas, "U.S. Drug Control Policy," November, 1996. www.fpif.org/briefs/vol1/drugs_body.html.

25. Quoted in Jack Nelson and Ronald J. Ostrow, "Illegal Drug Scene Spurs Rise in Police Corruption," *Los Angeles Times,* June 13, 1998, p. 1.

26. U.S. Constitution, Fourth Amendment.

27. President George W. Bush, State of the Union Address, January 20, 2004. www.whitehouse.gov/stateoftheunion/2004/index.html.

Chapter 4: Other Approaches to the Drug Problem

28. Ethan Nadelmann, "Ending the War on Drugs," *Lapis Magazine,* 2001. www.lindesmith.org/library/nadelmann_lapis2.cfm.

29. Quoted in David F. Musto, *The American Disease: Origins of Narcotics Control.* New York: Oxford University Press, 1987, p. 267.

30. Kleiman, *Against Excess,* p. 269.

31. Michael Massing, *The Fix: Under the Nixon Administration, America Had an Effective Drug Policy. We Should Restore It,* New York: Simon & Schuster, 1998, p. 11.

32. Quoted in Husak, *Legalize This!,* p. 151.

Chapter 5: A Closer Look at Legalization

33. Quoted in Church, "Thinking the Unthinkable."

34. Bennett, Di Iulio Jr., and Walters, *Body Count,* p. 146.

35. David Boaz, "The Legalization of Drugs: Decriminalization," *Vital Speeches of the Day,* August 15, 1988, p. 656.

36. Robert MacCoun and Peter Reuter, "Cocaine, Marijuana, and Heroin," *The American Prospect,* June 3, 2002, p. 25.

37. Husak, *Legalize This!,* p. 57.

38. Husak, *Legalize This!,* pp. 69–70.

Chapter 6: Legalizing Marijuana

39. Kleiman, *Against Excess,* p. 253.

40. Ira Glasser, "Spotlight: Why Marijuana Law Reform Should Matter to You." *National ACLU Member's Bulletin,* Spring 1998. "Marijuana Laws Should Be Relaxed."

41. Quoted in Horowitz, "Drugs Are Bad: The Drug War Is Worse," p. 32.

42. Office of National Drug Control Policy, National Youth Anti-Drug Media Campaign, "Pregnancy" advertisement that premiered January 2003. www.mediacampaign.org/mg/television.html.

Organizations
to Contact

Drug Policy Alliance

70 West 36th Street
16th Floor
New York, NY 10018
(212) 613-8020
www.drugpolicy.org

The Drug Policy Alliance seeks to reform drug laws and pro-
motes alternatives to the drug war such as harm reduction and
decriminalization of marijuana. The alliance is directed by
prominent drug reform spokesman Ethan Nadelmann and
funded in part by billionaire philanthropist George Soros.

Drug Watch International

P.O. Box 45218
Omaha, NE 68145
(402) 384-9212
www.drugwatch.org

Drug Watch International supports law enforcement, research,
and education efforts to end illegal drug use and underage
drinking.

Families Against Mandatory Minimums (FAMM)

1612 K Street, NW
Suite 700
Washington, DC 20006
(202) 822-6700
www.famm.org

FAMM members include prisoners and their families, judges, lawyers, criminal justice experts, and others who work to challenge mandatory minimum sentencing policies for drug offenses. The group's Web site includes brief biographies of people serving prison time under mandatory sentencing laws.

The National Center on Addiction and Substance Abuse at Columbia University (CASA)

633 Third Avenue
19th Floor
New York, NY 10017-6706
(212) 841-5200
www.CASAColumbia.org

CASA brings together experts from fields such as public health, criminal law, and government to study and combat the abuse of illegal drugs, alcohol, and cigarettes. The Web site includes links to articles and studies on substance abuse in the United States.

National Organization for the Reform of Marijuana Laws (NORML)

1600 K Street, NW
Suite 501
Washington, DC 20006-2832
(202) 483-5500
www.norml.org

NORML is a pro-marijuana group that lobbies for reform of state and federal marijuana laws. The group supports decriminalization and a legally controlled market for adult use of marijuana.

Office of National Drug Control Policies (ONDCP)

www.whitehousedrugpolicy.gov

A branch of the Executive Office of the President, ONDCP sets policies and objectives for U.S. drug control programs. The Web site includes fact sheets and statistics on common illegal drugs and a link to the National Youth Media Campaign page, which features current TV and radio ads aimed at stopping teen drug use.

Partnership for a Drug-Free America

405 Lexington Avenue
Suite 1601
New York, NY 10174
(212) 922-1560
www.drugfreeamerica.org

Founded by professionals from the advertising and communications industries, the Partnership is a drug-education group that aims to prevent teens and young people from using drugs. The group sponsors the largest media campaign against drug use in the country.

Students for a Sensible Drug Policy (SSDP)

1623 Connecticut Avenue, NW
Suite 300
Washington, DC 20009
(202) 293-4414
www.ssdp.org

SSDP is a drug reform group run by students on college campuses across the country. The group focuses on issues that directly affect young people, including drug testing in schools, drug education programs, and policies that deny college financial aid to anyone with a drug-related conviction.

For Further Reading

Books

Scott Barbour, ed., *Drug Legalization.* San Diego, CA: Greenhaven, 2000. Part of the Current Controversies series for young adult readers, the book is a collection of articles by prominent legalization supporters and their opponents who defend current drug policies.

Mathea Falco, *The Making of a Drug-Free America, Programs That Work.* New York: Times, 1994. Falco has years of experience implementing drug control and public health policies for the government and nonprofit groups. The book describes alternatives to the law enforcement approach to drug control in prevention, education, and treatment that are working in local communities across the nation.

Ted Gottfried, *Should Drugs Be Legalized?* Brookfield, CT: Twenty-First Century, 2000. In this book for young adult readers, Gottfried lays out the evidence for and against drug legalization with concise descriptions of various illegal drugs, current drug laws, the history of the U.S. drug war, and its global impact.

Jennifer Lawler, *Drug Legalization, A Pro/Con Issue.* Berkeley Heights, NJ: Enslow, 1999. Lawler presents a book for young adult readers with summaries of the major arguments for and against legalization and other approaches to drug control, including harm reduction.

Susan Neiburg Terkel, *The Drug Laws, A Time for Change?* New York: Franklin Watts, 1997. In this book designed for young adult readers, Neiburg Terkel clearly describes current drug laws and policies and lays out the arguments for reforms such as needle exchange and medical marijuana, as well as the legal, ethical, and health questions surrounding legalization.

Patsy Westcott, *Why Do People Take Drugs?* Austin, TX: Raintree Steck-Vaughn, 2001. Part of the Exploring Tough Issues series for young readers, this book includes simple descriptions of various drugs, the people who use them, and the laws governing their use.

Web Sites

Drug Sense/Media Awareness Project (http://drugsense.org) Drug Sense is a nonprofit group opposed to the war on drugs. Its Media Awareness Project calls attention to errors and distortions of drug issues that appear in the popular media. The Web site includes a database of current news and opinion on drug reform issues, as well as a weekly online publication.

Frontline: Drug Wars (www.npr.org/about/press/001005. frontline.html) This Web page is connected with a two-part series, exploring the history of the drug wars, that aired in 2000 on PBS's *Frontline*. It includes interviews with drug traffickers, law enforcement agents, a former drug czar, and other major players, as well as timelines, video clips, articles, discussion guides, and interactive quizzes.

KQED-TV/You Decide: Marijuana Legalization (www.kq ed.org/topics/news/perspectives/youdecide/pop/marijuana) Sponsored by public television station KQED in San Francisco, this online activity challenges participants to weigh evidence for and against marijuana legalization and cast a series of five votes. The final vote is recorded in an online survey.

Monitoring the Future Study (www.monitoringthefuture.org) Monitoring the Future is an ongoing study that tracks the behaviors, attitudes, and values of U.S. high school students, college students, and young adults. The Web site includes survey results on drug use from 1975 to the present, with overviews of key findings and sample questionnaires.

Substance Abuse and Mental Health Services Administration (Office of Applied Studies) (http://oas.samhsa.gov) SAMHSA's Office of Applied Studies provides access to the latest national data on illegal drug, alcohol, and tobacco use from the National Survey on Drug Use and Health (NS-DUH), with overviews and related articles.

United States Drug Enforcement Administration (www.dea.gov) DEA's Web site includes descriptions of current government drug control strategies in the United States and around the world, with articles, personal testimonies, and statistics. The Student Resource page features government-sponsored drug education and prevention information.

Works Consulted

Books

Dan Baum, *Smoke and Mirrors: The War on Drugs and the Politics of Failure.* Boston: Little Brown, 1996. A journalistic retelling, based on interviews with former government officials and other important figures, of how the drug war escalated from the 1970s to the present.

William J. Bennett, John J. Di Iulio Jr., and John P. Walters, *Body Count: Moral Poverty . . . and How to Win America's War Against Crime and Drugs.* New York: Simon & Schuster, 1996. The authors, including current and former national "drug czars," describe the violent crime and drug abuse among young people in America's inner cities and attribute these problems to "moral poverty," the lack of loving, capable adults who teach them right from wrong.

Alan Bock, *Waiting to Inhale: The Politics of Medical Marijuana.* Santa Ana, CA: Seven Locks, 2000. The story of California's efforts to pass and implement the state's medical marijuana initiative. Bock, a journalist and editorial writer who covered the issue for many years, paints a sympathetic portrait of the medical marijuana movement.

Dirk Chase Eldredge, *Ending the War on Drugs: A Solution for America.* Bridgehampton, NY: Bridge Works, 1998. This book by a former businessman and social conservative explores the social, economic, and health-related costs of the war on drugs and advocates a policy of government-controlled drug legalization.

Mike Gray, *Drug Crazy: How We Got into This Mess & How We Can Get Out.* New York: Random House, 1998. A feature film director and writer, Gray relates dramatic stories of the excesses of the drug war and focuses on some of the major players, including Pablo Escobar, the brutal Colombian drug lord, and Dr. Lester Grinspoon, a crusader for medical marijuana.

Douglas Husak, *Legalize This! the case for decriminalizing drugs.* London: Verso, 2002. A professor of law and philosophy, Husak makes an argument for legalizing drugs based on the view that punitive U.S. drug policies are unjust and inflict more damage on American society than drug use itself.

Mark A. Kleiman, *Against Excess: Drug Policy for Results.* New York: BasicBooks, 1992. Drug policy analyst Kleiman examines the excesses of drug abuse and U.S. drug control policies and considers practical approaches to limiting the harm caused by both.

Robert J. MacCoun and Peter Reuter, *Drug War Heresies: Learning from Other Vices; Times, & Places.* Cambridge, UK: Cambridge University Press, 2001. The authors explore the costs and benefits of various approaches to drug control, including legalization and harm reduction. The book draws on the experiences of foreign countries as well as U.S. efforts to regulate alcohol, gambling, and prostitution.

Michael Massing, *The Fix.* New York: Simon & Schuster, 1998. Having reported on illegal drug issues for more than a decade, Massing believes that a small population of hardcore heroin and cocaine users are the nation's real drug problem. The book considers the public health approach to addiction first adopted during the Nixon years and how this could be revived today.

David F. Musto, *The American Disease: Origins of Narcotic Control.* New York: Oxford University Press, 1987. Musto presents a comprehensive history of drug use and attitudes toward it from the eighteenth century to the crack scare of the 1980s, with an analysis of how these attitudes have impacted the nation's drug control policies.

Periodicals

David Boaz, "The Legalization of Drugs: Decriminalization," *Vital Speeches of the Day,* August 15, 1988.

George J. Church, "Thinking the Unthinkable: As Frustration Mounts over a Failed Policy, Serious People Are Asking: Why Not End the Crime and Profits by Making Drugs Legal?" *Time,* May 30, 1988, p. 12.

Gary Gately, "Baltimore Struggles to Battle Witness Intimidation," *Boston Globe,* February 12, 2005, p. A3.

Ira Glasser, "Spotlight: Why Marijuana Reform Should Matter to You," *National ACLU Member's Bulletin,* Spring 1998.

Craig Horowitz, "Drugs Are Bad: The Drug War Is Worse," *New York Magazine,* February 5, 1996. pp. 22–32.

Robert MacCoun and Peter Reuter, "Cocaine, Marijuana, and Heroin," *The American Prospect,* June 3, 2002, pp. 25–28.

Jack Nelson and Ronald J. Ostrow, "Illegal Drug Scene Spurs Rise in Police Corruption," *Los Angeles Times,* June 13, 1998, p. 1.

New York Times, "No Change in Basics: Bush Rejects Any Fundamental Shift, Instead Vowing Unprecedented Vigor," September 6, 1989, p. A11.

Allison North Jones, "The Media Business: Advertising; Strong Views, Pro and Con, on Ads Linking Drug Use to Terrorism," *New York Times,* April 2, 2002, p. C7.

Charles B. Rangel, "Why Drug Legalization Should Be Opposed," *Criminal Justice Ethics,* Summer-Fall 1998, p. 2.

Elaine Shannon, "A Losing Battle: Despite Billions of Dollars and More Than a Million Arrests, the War on Drugs Has Barely Dented Addiction or Violent Crime," *Time,* December 3, 1990, p. 44.

Christopher S. Wren, "The Opposing Camps Square Off at a Congressional Hearing About Drug Legalization," *New York Times,* June 20, 1999, p. 28.

Internet Sources

Peter Andreas, "U.S. Drug Control Policy," November 1996. www.fpif.org/briefs/vol1/drugs_body.html.

Bureau of Justice Statistics: United States Department of Justice, "Drugs and Crime Facts," 2002. www.ojp.usdoj.gov/bjs/dcf/contents.htm.

Families Against Mandatory Minimums, "Mandatory Sentencing Was Once America's Law-and-Order Panacea: Here's Why It's Not Working: Primer on Mandatory Minimums," www.famm.org/ac_beginners_guide.htm.

Human Rights Watch, "United States: Racial Disparities in the War on Drugs," May 2000. www.hrw.org/reports/2000/usa.

L.D. Johnston, P.M. O'Malley, J.G. Bachman, & J.E. Schulenberg, *Monitoring the Future National Survey Results on Drug Use, 1975–2003: vol. I: Secondary School Students.* Bethesda, MD: National Institute on Drug Abuse, 2003. www.monitoringthefuture.org.

Harry G. Levine and Craig Reinarman, "The Politics of America's Latest Drug Scare," in Richard O. Curry, ed., *Freedom at Risk: Secrecy, Censorship, and Repression in the 1980s.* Philadelphia: Temple University Press, 1988, Chapter 17. www.psychedelic-library.org/drug_politics.htm.

Ethan Nadelmann, "An End to Marijuana Prohibition: The Drive to Legalize Picks Up," *National Review,* July 12, 2004. www.mpp.org/USA/news_7835.html.

———, "Ending the War on Drugs," *Lapis Magazine,* 2001. www.lindesmith.org/library/nadelmann_lapis2.cfm.

National Drug Strategy Network, "State Agents Raid Cannabis Buyers' Club in San Francisco," September 1996. www.ndsn.org/sept96/cbc.html.

National Institute on Drug Abuse (NIDA), "NIDA Info Facts," www.drugabuse.gov.

Office of National Drug Control Policy, "The President's National Drug Control Strategy," March 2004. www.whitehousedrugpolicy.gov/publications/policy/ndcs04.

Craig Reinarman and Harry G. Levine, "The Construction of America's Crack Crisis," 1995. www.drugtext.org/library/articles/craig2.html.

David Risley, "Mandatory Minimum Sentences: An Overview," DrugWatch International, May 2000. www.drugwatch.org/Mandatory%20Minimum%20Sentences.htm.

Hanna Rosin, "The Return of Pot," *The New Republic,* February 17, 1997. www.tnr.com/archive/1997/0297/021797/rosin 02179.html.

Patrick Stephens, "Drugs and Terrorism: They're Not the Same Thing," 2002. www.objectivistcenter.org/mediacenter/articles/ pstephens_drugs-terrorism.asp.

Subcommittee on Criminal Justice, Drug Policy and Human Resources, Committee on Government Reform, U.S. House of Representatives, "Federal Law Enforcement at the Borders and Ports of Entry: Challenges and Solutions," July 2002, Report 107–794. www.house.gov/reform.

Substance Abuse and Mental Health Services Administration, "National Survey on Drug Use and Health," 2003. www. oas.samhsa.gov/nhsda.htm#NHSDAinfo.

Wikipedia, "Controlled Substances Act," http://en.wikipedia. org/wiki/Controlled_Substances_Act.

Speeches and Testimony

President George W. Bush, State of the Union Address, January 20, 2004. www.whitehouse.gov/stateoftheunion/2004/ index.html.

Bruce D. Glasscock, "Testimony Before Congress: Glasscock Testimony on Decriminalization of Illegal Drugs," International Association of Police Chiefs, July 13, 1999. www.theiacp. org/documents/index.cfm?document_id=60&fuseaction= document&subtype_id=1.

Anthony M. Kennedy, Speech at the American Bar Association Annual Meeting, August 9, 2003. www.supremecourtus. gov/publicinfo/speeches/sp_08-09-03.html.

Index

Picture Credits

About the Author

Meryl Loonin is a writer who works on educational media and curriculum projects. She has a background in documentary film and television production and a master's degree in education. She has produced and developed many films and television documentaries on topics such as human evolution, Latin American literature, family life in the former Soviet Union, and the Cold War race to build the hydrogen bomb. Ms. Loonin also has a strong interest in helping young people publish their own work. She has collaborated on Web sites, videos, and books of creative work by and for kids. Ms. Loonin's first book for Lucent, *Multicultural America,* was published in 2004. She lives in Lexington, Massachusetts, with her husband, Neil, and two children, Hana and Jonah.

Woodland High School